Skin Prick Testing
in
Clinical Practice

"The Cornerstone in Allergy Diagnosis"

Skin Prick Testing
in
Clinical Practice

Mary J Brydon
RGN OHNC FRCN

Allergy Nurse Practitioner
Primary Care Norfolk

Foreword by Stephen T Holgate
BSc MD DSc FRCP FRCPE
CBiol FIBiol FRCPath FMedSci

Divisional Director
Medical Research Council (MRC)
Clinical Professor of Immunopharmacology,
Southampton University Hospitals NHS Trust
Southampton, UK.

Published by NADAAS

N.A.D.A.A.S.
Norfolk Allergy Diagnostic And Advisory Service

Norwich, Norfolk, UK

ISBN 0-9537646-0-5

© Mary J Brydon 2000
NADAAS
36 Glenalmond
Eaton
Norwich
Norfolk NR4 6AG

First published 2000

Designed, printed and bound in the UK by:

East Anglian Engraving Ltd.
Norwich, Norfolk.

DEDICATION

Dedicated to Derek

"No matter what

accomplishments you make,

somebody helps you"

Althea Gibson

ACKNOWLEDGEMENTS

In preparing this book I have been most fortunate in receiving support and help from many people and in particular would like to express my gratitude to the following:

To my husband Derek for his constant support and encouragement and for the preparation and proof reading of the first drafts.

To Professor Holgate for his support and interest over many years and for writing the foreword to this book.

To Louise Zucchi for proof reading the final draft.

To the young "Professor" Lewis aged two, to Harry, Charles, Edward and James aged between two and four, and to Emily aged five, thank you for being such delightful patients. Also a thank you to their mothers for allowing their children to be photographed.

To Allergy Therapeutics Ltd. for their educational grant.

In addition I would like to acknowledge the following for their kind permission to reproduce or adapt material from the following books.

Blackwell Science Ltd	Essential Allergy	Niels Mygind et al
	Food Allergy	Metcalf, Simpson & Simon
	Food & Food Additive Intolerance	
	in Childhood	T J David
Mosby (Harcourt Press)	Allergy	S T Holgate & M Church
	Atlas of Allergy	Philip Fireman & R Slavin
Dr Carlos Perez-Santos	Allergy to Animals, for his generous	
	"use what ever you need"	
Dr T S Smith	Emory University, USA	
Nursing Standard	for permission to reprint Figure 28	
Practice Nursing	for permission to reprint the Allergy Protocol	

WHY READ THIS BOOK?

"Read not to contradict and confute, nor to believe and take for granted, nor to find talk and discourse, but to weigh and consider."

Francis Bacon

FOREWORD

There can hardly be a single person who does not either suffer from allergy or know someone in their family who has an allergic disease. The last two decades have witnessed a spectacular rise in the incidence of allergic disease to a point where it should now be considered as a public health problem. It follows that, in addition to the expression of susceptibility genes that creates the familial clustering of allergic disorders, there are important environmental factors that are necessary for the allergic phenotype to be expressed in different organs. While these include exposure to allergens in the indoor and outdoor environments, other important environmental factors include exposure to viral and bacterial infections, air pollutants and dietary constituents.

There remains considerable confusion in the minds of some health professionals and most of the public over what the term allergy means. From a medical standpoint, allergy occurs when the immune system becomes polarised in such a way that the allergic antibody IgE is generated (immediate hypersensitivity) or a specific type of inflammatory response in an organ is driven by T-lymphocytes and/or immune complexes containing the offending allergen (the Arthus reaction and delayed hypersensitivity). These should be differentiated from the many other conditions in which the environment may play a role and where various forms of chemical intolerance occur e.g. migraine, irritable bowel syndrome, chronic fatigue syndrome. By far the most common type of allergy involves allergen-specific IgE causing such disorders as asthma, rhinitis, conjunctivitis, food allergy, sinusitis and some skin reactions e.g. urticaria. Pivotal to establishing an accurate diagnosis of these conditions and, in particular, pinpointing the causative allergens is the role of the skin prick test.

In this book, Mary Brydon clarifies any misconceptions about allergy skin prick testing and discusses how the test should be interpreted in the context of a patient's medical history. The book also contains valuable guidance on how the skin prick test should be carried out and the results measured. After 16 years as an allergy nurse practitioner, Mary Brydon has produced an informative and balanced review of a key component of good allergy practice. The subject area covered by this book should be of particular value to those wishing to use the test in either primary or secondary care medical settings and should help health professionals sort out specific allergen hypersensitivity from disorders frequently labelled as allergic which are in fact due to other factors including food and chemical intolerance.

Stephen T Holgate

Contents

INTRODUCTION

Atopy is defined as the production of specific IgE in response to exposure to common environmental allergens, such as house dust mite, grass and cat. Being atopic is strongly associated with allergic disease such as asthma, hay-fever and eczema. However, not everyone with atopy develops clinical manifestations of allergy, and not everyone with a clinical syndrome compatible with allergic disease can be shown to be atopic when tested for specific IgE to a wide range of environmental allergens (Jarvis & Burney, 1997).

The prevalence of diseases associated with atopy has increased in many parts of the world over the past 20 to 30 years and manifestations of allergic diseases are observed in 35% of the general population. The European White Paper on Allergy (1997) recognises allergic diseases as a public health problem in Europe. In the foreword of the White Paper, Flynn states that "despite their relatively low mortality, allergic diseases represent a growing socio-economic burden in Europe".

Despite its frequency, seasonal rhinitis (hay-fever) may appear to many as merely a nuisance. Hay-fever and eczema are important causes of morbidity, being responsible for reduced quality of life and for a substantial proportion of health service use, particularly in primary care (Jarvis & Burney, 1997). In spite of this, during the first half of the 20th century allergic diseases ranked rather low in the priorities of public health authorities. Fortunately this attitude of "benign neglect" has started to change, with an increasing emphasis being placed on disease prevention rather than therapy alone.

However, before one can discuss prevention and avoidance strategies with the sufferer it is important to determine their atopic status and to identify what their allergies are and which allergens are causing their symptoms. This starts with a clear and precise clinical history, which must be critically evaluated at the same time as measuring specific IgE. These, together with physical examination and various other diagnostic assessments, will lead to a better understanding of the allergic patient.

The European White Paper states that the GP as the primary provider of health care is increasingly the model being implemented across Europe for the care of the allergic patient. As a consequence of this "new" awareness it is hoped that many professionals will become involved in skin prick testing, which Mygind regards as *"the cornerstone in allergy diagnosis"*. Much emphasis is being placed on the practical aspects of the testing procedure, and whilst the technique of skin prick testing is relatively simple to perform and an easily acquired skill there are other issues to be considered.

In the teaching of the technique equal emphasis should be given to the theory and understanding of the principles and objectives of skin prick testing and the ensuing results. Skin prick testing is only of real value when it is integrated into an holistic provision of care for the allergic sufferer, which essentially must include protected time for taking the history, disease management, avoidance strategies, treatment management and compliance. Educating the patients and their families is as important as educating the professional.

The purpose of this book is to provide a better understanding about what the test is demonstrating and how better to interpret the results, and in so doing fulfil the Royal College of Nursing's motto *"Tradiamus Lampada"*.

Author's Note:
The reader will find that some information is repeated across chapters. This is deliberate so that the reader referring to one chapter in isolation obtains a comprehensive picture.

CHAPTER ONE

Skin Prick Testing

History

Charles Blackley, a printer and engraver by trade, had a keen interest in sciences such as botany, microscopy and chemistry. In 1858 he opened a homeopathic practice in Manchester. It was in 1865 that he first described skin testing when he placed pollen from rye grass on abraded skin and reported a weal and flare response. Forty two years later in 1907 a distinguished Austrian paediatrician, Clement Von Pirquet, developed the method of testing further by introducing scratch testing for tuberculosis. A year later in 1908 the French physician Charles Mantoux devised the intracutaneous test, also for tuberculosis.

Following the discovery of histamine in the 1900s researchers focused on its role in allergy and allergic disease. In 1927 Sir Thomas Lewis described the "triple response" (local vasodilation, flare, and oedema) of skin to mechanical stimulation. First with light stroking producing pallor due to the constriction of the capillaries within 15–20 seconds and then with firmer pressure resulting in a red line, this time due to capillary dilation. Eventually, with very firm pressure, producing a weal due to the release of histamine and other mediators from the mast cells.

Bela Schick, an American paediatrician born in Hungary and a contemporary of Von Pirquet, introduced the Schick test (intracutaneous test) for diphtheria in 1905. He worked with Von Pirquet at the Paediatric Clinic in Vienna studying serum sickness. Together they introduced the term "allergy". Robert Anderson Cooke, an American physician, adapted and introduced the intracutaneous test for the diagnosis and identification of allergens. Both the scratch test and intracutaneous test have high risk problems which include fatalities and false-positive reactions. In consequence, in the UK, these methods of allergy testing have become obsolete. In 1930, the English physician John Freeman and Sir Thomas Lewis introduced the prick test, which became widespread in the 1970s after its modification by Pepys. Since then it has remained *"The Cornerstone of Allergy Diagnosis"* (Mygind, 1996).

What is allergy?

Allergy is a term which describes an immune response in the body, to a substance which in itself is not harmful. This response and reaction give rise to symptoms and disease in a predisposed individual (Mygind, 1996). The term allergy initially embraced immunology, but now is focused on the host tissue-damaging or irritation effects on immunological responses (Holgate & Church, 1993).

Predisposed individuals are described as being atopic i.e. they have a condition known as atopy. Atopy is not an illness but an inherited feature, which in turn makes individuals more likely to develop an allergic disorder. Atopy tends to run in families.

Basic principles

Atopic individuals have the ability to produce an allergy antibody called immunoglobulin E (IgE) when they come into contact with a particular substance (allergen).

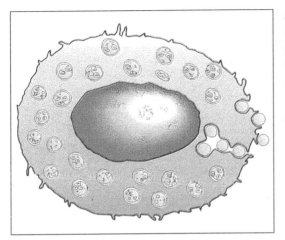

Figure 1
Human mast cell with secretory granules, showing the characteristic laminar structure.
Degranulation is indicated on the right of the cell.
(Courtesy of Blackwell Science Ltd.)

This ability to mount IgE-mediated responses to allergens is a prerequisite for the development of positive allergen tests. In the human body there are 5,000 – 12,000 mast cells per cubic millimetre, evenly distributed and frequently observed in close anatomic association with blood vessels and nerves (Bousquet, 1993).

The skin prick test is an efficient and simple method of introducing a small amount of allergen into the body which enables the measurement of specific IgE. The immediate reaction to the skin prick test is dependent on mast cells that are rapidly degranulated after this form of allergen challenge. Histamine release begins about 5 minutes after allergen challenge and peaks at about 30 minutes.

Thus the atopic status of an individual can be determined by skin prick testing with inhalant or food allergens, which in turn may explain the cause of their symptoms within the respiratory, skin or gastro-intestinal organs. The IgE antibodies, which may be produced locally, can be distributed to all parts of the body by plasma and tissue fluid, resulting in a generalised sensitisation. In the UK, atopy is conventionally defined as one or more positive skin tests.

Purpose of testing

What is the purpose of allergy skin prick testing? "It is necessary to select IgE allergic patients and to determine sensitivity to one or more allergens so that the correct treatment can be started at an early stage and the risk of chronic inflammation and tissue destruction reduced. This is particularly important for the prognosis of the hyperreactive state" (Holgate & Church, 1993). In other words is the patient atopic, and secondly is the patient allergic to a specific allergen?

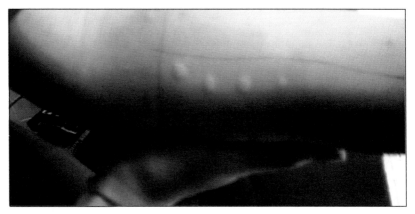

Figure 2 Weal and flare response in an adult.

If the patient is allergic, the skin prick test response produces a weal and flare reaction (oedema and erythema) to the specific allergen being tested and is regarded as a measurement of mast cell fixed IgE antibody.

This weal and flare reaction can easily be measured. However the results of the test are dependent, as stated before, on the mast cell's releasability of mediators and of the tissue sensitivity to them.

The assessment by skin prick testing of the relative contribution of allergic factors in the development of a given individual's symptoms is essential in order to confirm the clinical history and to underpin advice on allergen avoidance and treatment management (See Table 1). "Only in a few cases does the medical history *per se* allow a firm conclusive diagnosis. An example of this is allergy to birch pollen, where the symptoms appear in the birch pollen season in Northern Europe, against a back ground of perennial intolerance to nuts and fresh fruit" (Holgate & Church, 1993).

Table 1 Reasons for performing skin tests

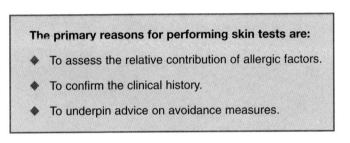

The primary reasons for performing skin tests are:
- To assess the relative contribution of allergic factors.
- To confirm the clinical history.
- To underpin advice on avoidance measures.

Unfortunately it has been the author's experience that some patients who have had skin tests in the past have neither been told what it is they are allergic to, nor given an allergen avoidance plan, which is frustrating for them and their doctors.

"Performing a test but not acting on the results is a waste of everyone's time. On the other hand before acting on the results, clinicians need to understand how the test performs and what a positive result really means" (Frew, 1992).

Other factors to be considered when electing to carry out skin prick testing are listed in Table 2 overleaf.

It is important that skin prick testing is not carried out in isolation. It must be preceded by a clear and precise history and the history should indicate the allergens to be selected for testing, the results of which will provide supportive evidence, positive or negative.

(Please see interpretation of results on page 40 and refer to Appendices 2 & 3 for the NADAAS Allergy Assessment Questionnaires and Protocol.)

Table 2 Smith's Principles of Allergy Testing

◆ Allergy testing is not likely to be useful for diagnosis in patients whose symptoms are unlikely to be mediated by IgE antibodies.

◆ Allergy testing with materials not shown to be allergenic is unlikely to produce clinical useful information.

◆ Degranulation of mast cells may be caused by mechanisms other than that which is IgE-dependent.

◆ Tests that document the presence of IgE antibodies do not necessarily predict that these antibodies are involved in clinical illness.

◆ Testing using agents unlikely to cause IgE-mediated symptoms is unlikely to produce positive results.

The skin prick test has a particular value in the management of asthma, rhinitis and many other conditions, secretory otitis media being an example. In a study carried out on 200 children, aged 3 to 8 years, with a diagnosis of secretory otitis media, two thirds were skin test positive. Anti-allergy therapy was associated with an improvement in hearing and a significant decrease in symptoms (Scadding, 1993).

Who can be tested & what influences the test results?

Numerous factors can influence the reactivity of the skin to skin prick testing, which includes site on the body, age, sex, race, ingestion of drugs, circadian rhythm and user technique. Other factors influencing skin reactivity to an allergen include: the amount of allergen injected; the number, degree of sensitisation and reliability of cutaneous mast cells; and the reactivity of the skin to mediators released from mast cells, particularly histamine (Bousquet, 1993).

Skin prick testing may be performed at any time of life. However, the skin reaction is less pronounced in smaller children and the elderly. It is often thought that small infants do not show positive skin tests, and that they only react with a flare rather than a weal

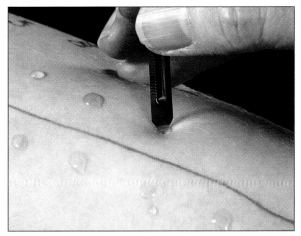

Figure 3 Skin Prick Test.

and flare. However, positive reactions are found in infants just a few weeks old, but the reaction is smaller than would be expected in an older child (Hide, 1989).

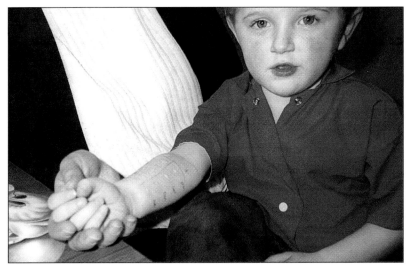

Figure 4 Example of response on a young child.

Weal diameters were found to increase with age and were greater in the atopic compared with non-atopic infants from age 4 months (Van Asperen, 1984), and it was found that positive skin prick tests occurred at the age of 3 months (Taylor, 1973). Skin prick tests are of value in infancy and in particular the results correlate well with immediate food allergic reactions.

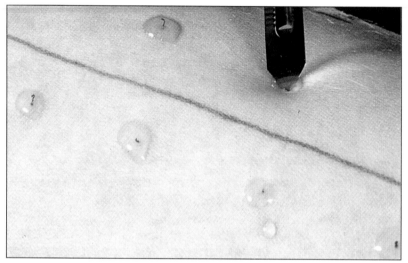

Figure 5 Typical reaction to trauma of test on elderly skin.

Ageing skin can influence the degree of response as the weal reaction decreases with age. It has been the author's experience that ageing and thinning skin shows a marked vesicle response without flare. On skin testing one should not draw blood. If patients of any age group bleed easily at the site of the test then it is an indication that the operator has been too firm or heavy handed in performing the test and this may result in unnecessary trauma.

Nevertheless, in some elderly patients with ageing skin, the gentlest of pricks can draw a small amount of blood as illustrated in figure 5. Once the excess solution has been blotted off as shown in figure 6, there should be no further traces of blood.

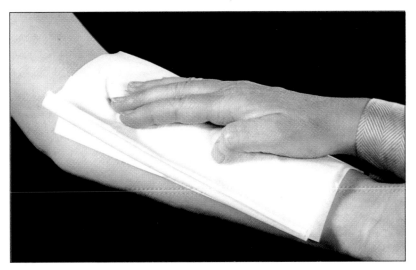

Figure 6 Blotting excess solutions.

Contrary to this, if a practitioner is getting consistent negative responses from a series of patients, then this could indicate that the operator's technique is too light or that the solutions have lost their potency.

Variations in potency between allergen extracts from different manufacturers is another well recognised influence on skin test results (Björkstén, 1984).

Skin testing at different times of the day on the same subject may give inconsistent results. One influence is the patient circadian rhythm (Cromia, 1952). The responses are low in the morning, increasing in the afternoon and peaking in the early evening. However, it is believed that this was not of great practical importance (Hide, 1989). Nevertheless it is well to be mindful that in retesting the patient at different times, particularly in clinical trials, the circadian rhythm may have some influence.

In addition to the circadian rhythm having an influence on the skin test outcome, body temperature should also be considered. If the patient is cold or the room is cold then this can inhibit a skin response.

The influence of the menstrual cycle on skin prick test reactions shows a significant increase in weal and flare size on day 12-16 of the cycle, corresponding to ovulation and peak oestrogen and low progesterone levels (Kalogeromitros, 1995). The authors concluded that the phase of the menstrual cycle is another factor that may influence skin test results, and that the phases of the menstrual cycle may theoretically be due to changes in vascular permeability and vasodilation mediated directly or indirectly by changes in the oestrogen and progesterone levels.

Female sex hormones can also affect immune function influencing T cell populations, the production of specific antibodies, clotting factors, pro-inflammatory mediators and mast cell degranulation.

There are inconsistent reports of racial differences in the prevalence of atopy and atopic disease. In differences observed between races it is difficult to determine whether they reflect differences in genetic predisposition, exposure to environmental risk factors or cultural attitude to disease (Jarvis & Burney, 1998).

Total IgE levels have been reported to be higher in black people than in white people in America (Grundbacher, 1975) and South Africa (Orron & Dowdle, 1975). The National Health Survey showed a slightly higher prevalence of positive skin tests amongst black people than white people (Vital & Health Statistics, 1986). Skin testing should not be performed on anatomical locations with eczema or in patients with obvious dermatographism (see figure 7) because of their heightened level of skin reactivity and the potential for false positive results.

Anti-allergenic drug treatment may significantly suppress the early phase response (EPR) to skin prick testing. A general rule is that treatment with conventional, relatively short-acting antihistamines should be discontinued 3 to 5 days prior to the skin prick tests. Hydroxyzine, Ketotifen and tricyclic anti-depressants should be stopped for 2 weeks. Long-acting non-sedating antihistamines, e.g. Astemizole suppresses the EPR for up to 2 months. [It is to

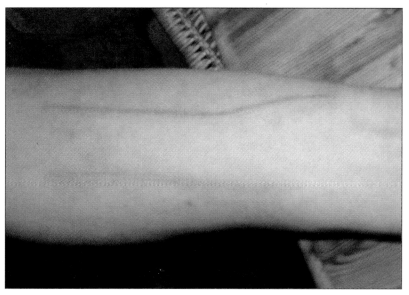

Figure 7 Example of dermatographism.

be noted that Astemizole will no longer be manufactured, however existing supplies are not being removed from pharmacies (Gottlieb, 1999)]. Bronchodilators, including Adrenaline, Theophylline and Oral β_2 Adrenergic agonists, have not been shown to significantly suppress the skin reaction to allergen or to histamine. Short courses of corticosteroids in doses equivalent to 30 mg of prednisone per day for a week do not significantly suppress the skin reaction, and there is no need to discontinue low-dose oral glucocorticosteroids (less than 10 mg of prednisolone per day).

The application of high-potency, topical corticosteroids to the test area decreases allergen induced weal and flare reactions and, to a minor degree, the histamine induced weal. This form of treatment should be avoided for 2–3 weeks prior to testing. Topical dermal anaesthetic creams inhibit the flare, but not the weal response to allergens and histamine. The sites used for skin testing can have an influence on skin test results. (Please see the section on the site to be tested, page 25.)

Reproducibility

"Any procedure of value has to satisfy the criteria of reproducibility, which in turn depends on three variables: the procedure, the practitioner and the patient... While skin test sensitivity can change, my experience is that repeated testing, using the same materials, with precisely the same method, ideally the same tester, gives remarkably reproducible results" (Hide, 1989). Of course not all skin prick testing will be carried out by a physician, and the task is frequently delegated to a nurse. It is essential that any nurse expected to perform skin testing should only do so following a period of clinical supervision in the technique before being deemed competent to practice the procedure and thus maintain reproducibility.

It is the author's view that if nurses are expected to only perform a skin test it is reducing their role in allergy to that of a technician, which is a disservice to the nurse. Ideally, nurses should be practitioners in their own right. Having nurses perform skin tests and then expecting them to advise on avoidance management and treatment compliance without recourse to the patient's history is counter productive.

Both in vivo and in vitro testing are readily available to physicians who may not be trained to order or perform these tests and to interpret their results appropriately. Manufacturers of allergen solutions have pointed out that diagnosis of allergy using in vivo or in vitro technology involves educated judgement and they have called for extensive user education programmes to bring about improved patient care (Daniel, 1990).

The performance of a test indicates the best it can do. The performance of a person doing the test limits how well the test actually performs in diagnosis (Smith, 1992).

CHAPTER TWO

Solutions
and the Lancet

Solutions for testing

In the past, extracts have often been impure so that a positive result was not necessarily a reaction to the major allergen. They could well have contained irritants. For these extracts the diluent used was normal saline. Whilst this was a safe substance to introduce into the body and was easily sterilised, it offered no resistance to bacterial or viral contamination of the allergen solution. For this reason a small amount of antiseptic material, usually phenol, was added. Although this protected the solution from contamination it did nothing to preserve the allergen added to the saline which is likely to change in chemical nature over a period of time. In order to stabilise the allergen, glycerine was added usually in a strength of 50%. Even if pure, the concentration of allergen in the bottle often varied leading to inconsistent results.

Manufacturers have made strenuous efforts to improve the quality of the extracts and it is only in recent years that a uniform method of testing and labelling of test solutions has been developed. The original standard of the Noon Unit was one millionth of the quantity of protein that could be extracted from 1 gram of pollen. Then a weight/volume system was devised where a given weight of dried extract was diluted in a given volume. This in turn is

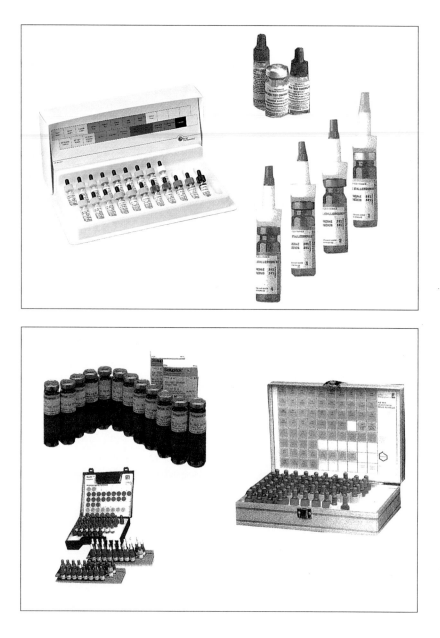

Figures 8 & 9 Examples of skin prick test solutions & kits.

being superseded by the expression of the protein-nitrogen units (PNU): 1 PNU = 0.00001 gram of protein-nitrogen. However none of the systems stated the content of the specific allergen.

The situation now is that the identification of major antigens (allergens) such as *Der p*1 in house dust mites (*Dermatophagoides pteronusinus*) and *Fel d* I from cats (*Felix domesticus*), has encouraged the development of immunological techniques which can demonstrate that the extracts actually contain the allergens which they are supposed to contain. The precise amount of the major allergen per batch is assessed by quantitative electrophoresis and other methods, as described later, for some of the common allergen extracts. The potency of the product is then compared with standard in house reference preparations by RAST inhibition or similar methods (see below).

Such tests will greatly improve the quality of materials that have all too often contained a high proportion of impurities, not necessarily antigenic. It is recommended that house dust solution should no longer be used as it is known to contain a proportion of cat allergen. The author's experience, on questioning the content of house dust solution, is to be told that it has a cocktail of many allergens, thus rendering the solution little better than tap water.

The extracts that are biologically tested (skin test titration) and RAST (immunochemical method) give the strength of the extract in, for example, biological units (BU/ml), Histamine Equivalent Potency (HEP), allergy units (AU/ml) as in the USA, or the Diagnostic Unit (DU). At the optimum diagnostic concentration (ODC) the products are assigned a potency of 10,000 DU. Standardised, high-quality extracts contain allergens and epitopes (portion of antigen which combines with the antibody) present in the native material and can now be assured to have a consistent overall potency. Their use will allow comparison between skin test results obtained in the same patient tested at intervals or in different patients, which is of particular importance in epidemiological studies. However, standardisation does not by itself confirm that a product is at the correct strength to provide a correct diagnosis. It only confirms batch to batch reproducibility. Some solutions which have been tested provide a product at the optimum concentration in order to minimise false negative reactions. Loss of potency can also occur due to incorrect storage, therefore all allergen extracts, when not in use, should be kept in a refrigertor at a temperature of 4°C. In the past it was not uncommon to see allergy kits sitting on a window sill in blazing sunlight or on a radiator shelf.

It is also important to check, regularly, for the "out of date" period of the allergen solution. This can vary from manufacturer to manufacturer. In addition it is important to realise that the expiry date and level of potency and consistency may vary once the allergen bottle has been opened and some solutions in reality may have less than 6 months shelf life. However, tests performed with concentrated extracts which if glycerinated are stable for at least a year if refrigerated (Smith, 1992).

The emphasis that manufacturers are now placing upon standardisation means that solutions are now being registered as pharmaceutical products. It is recommended that only those products with product licences should be used.

The Nordic Committee on Allergen Standardisation has proposed the use of fresh foods and other fresh materials for skin prick testing (because many allergens are not standardised). This method (Dreborg & Foucard, 1983) of pricking first the fruit and then the skin with the same lancet is not without risk, particularly for those patients with atopy or known anaphylaxis and should only be practised by those with the appropriate expertise.

Control solutions

The negative control

To evaluate unspecific reactions caused by the trauma of the skin induced by the test device (e.g. dermatographism), tests should be performed routinely with a negative control solution in parallel with the allergen to be tested. This with a negative control solution in parallel with the allergen to be tested. This is essential as in rare cases the patient may "react" to all the allergens tested. The negative control is the basic diluent of the allergens i.e. Glycerine 50% (allergen stabiliser) and normal saline.

It has been known for patients to be told that they are "allergic to everything" when in fact the response observed was due to dermatographism (see figure 7, page 13).

The positive control

To document normal reactivity of the skin, i.e. no major change in skin reactivity due to intake of anti-allergic drugs, skin tests should be performed with a positive control, e.g. histamine or mast cell secretagogues such as codeine or compound 48/80. Histamine dihydrochloride 10 mg/ml is recommended for use as a positive control (Dreborg, 1988).

The Lancet

When considering skin prick testing, the safety of the procedure is paramount. Intradermal testing has been associated with adverse reactions in up to 20% of subjects tested, while skin prick testing is almost without risk (Malling,1993).

Prick testing is the method currently considered to be the most valuable in the diagnosis of inhalant and food allergy with immediate symptoms. There are various ways in which the technique can be carried out and the use of these various techniques will give rise to varying results. In certain parts of the world multiple puncture techniques or linear scratches are still carried out, however in the United Kingdom the standard technique is the prick test.

There are two methods of skin prick testing, whereby a small amount of allergen can be introduced into the epidermis using either a sterile lancet or a hypodermic needle. Mygind describes the latter as the "modified" skin prick

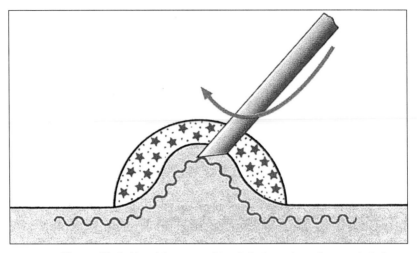

Figure 10   The modified skin prick test consists of placing a drop of concentrated extract on the skin and pricking with a lifting motion through the drop.
(Courtesy of Blackwell Science Ltd)

test, whereby the superficial layer of skin is lifted with a needle through the drop of allergen solution.The needle is inserted at approximately 55 degrees to the surface of the skin, as shown in figure 10. However, the disadvantage of a needle is that its use can result in an inconsistent depth of penetration.

On the other hand the lancet has a calibrated stylus of 1 mm and shoulders thus enabling consistency in the depth of penetration and a high degree of reproducibility. In this method the skin is punctured with the lancet being held perpendicular to the skin surface, as shown in figure 23, page 33, and is then withdrawn straight up. The lancet method is now commonly used in the UK and it should be noted that the majority of allergy publications use the term "skin prick testing" with little reference or distinction to "modified" skin prick testing.

It should also be noted that lancets are medical devices and as such should be registered. The package containing the lancet should carry a European C.E. mark.

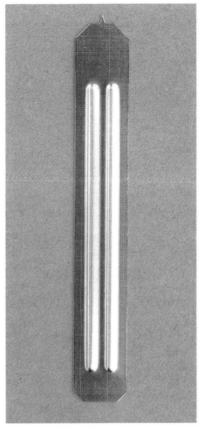

Figure 11 A Lancet

In the author's view the lancet is less frightening for children and those individuals with a needle phobia. It provides greater safety by preventing deep penetration, particularly in the case of a child pulling away because of fear or dislike of the "needle" and thus inadvertently causing an intra-dermal test. Also only about 5 µl of the allergen solution is introduced into the skin so the risk of an ana-phylactic reaction is extremely low. The test is quick and virtually pain-less (Mygind, 1996).

There are two schools of thought as to whether an individual lancet should be used for each allergen to be tested. The theory behind using a lancet for each allergen is to avoid a possible carry-over of the allergen solution to the next test site. However, it is the author's experi-ence in sixteen years of skin testing in a clinical setting that using one lancet and wiping the lancet thoroughly with a tissue or cotton wool has never resulted in the carry- over anticipated. In fact, on occasions, histamine has been placed in the middle of a number of selected allergens for testing. This was undertaken for experimental purposes and did not result in any carry-over to the subsequent (next) test site, which remained negative in the major-ity of cases. However where the next test site was a positive response after the histamine or the allergen challenge, the particular allergen was retested (on the opposite arm) in order to clarify whether it was the previous allergen or the histamine producing the reaction. In all the trials carried out by the author (unpublished) the histamine or allergen carry-over was not demonstrated. Indeed it is evident from discussions with colleagues in various parts of the UK and USA that the single lancet and wipe method appears to be used, extensively in clinical practice. However it is essential that in clinical trials one lancet is used for each allergen.

Skin testing is generally regarded as a relatively simple procedure to perform when carried out by skilled personnel. It is considered to be the safest and most widely used provocation test.

CHAPTER THREE

Procedure and Results

Preparation of patient

Prior to attending for a skin prick test, patients should be asked not to take any antihistamines or cough medicines for 4 to 5 days prior to the test. If patients are taking Astemizole (Hismanal) then this will need to be stopped 3 to 6 weeks prior to testing.

Some antidepressants and cough medicines may contain antihistamine. If patients are not sure which of their treatments to stop prior to testing, they should be advised to discuss matters with their local pharmacist, particularly if the test appointment is some time ahead.

It is also important to emphasise to asthma patients that they should **not** stop their inhaler use. Indeed patients using nasal corticosteroids need not stop their treatment.

However nasal antihistamine sprays i.e. Azelastine (Rhinolast) should be stopped, as there is a theoretical risk of a level of systemic absorption. Avoidance of topical steroid is also essential as outlined on page 13.

Equipment required for skin prick testing (Housekeeping)

Ideally skin prick tests should be performed in a room with natural daylight. This allows the results of the skin prick tests to be read much more easily. Artificial light can throw shadows. The room should be warm, and adequate seating should be provided for the patient and any accompanying family or carers.

Table 3 gives a list of recommended equipment and medication. It is essential that the equipment for testing is kept as clean as possible. The ruler and gauges should be washed regularly as they come in to contact with the patient's skin. Clinical wipes used during the course of the clinic day will be sufficient to clean the ruler and gauges between patients.

The gauges for measurement can be obtained from allergen solution manufacturers or pharmaceutical companies. If lancets are to be used, one per test solution, then it is essential when testing children that they are opened just prior to seeing the patient. The lancets should be covered until required (tissue or paper towel) and remain in their original package in order to avoid contamination. As in all good standards of hygiene practice the Sharps box should not be allowed to overspill and the lid should remain closed when not in use.

It is also important to ensure that all treatments such as hydrocortisone, antihistamine creams, tablets, medicines and Epinephrine (adrenaline) are in date and are kept to hand in a hygienic container.

It will be seen in Chapter 4 (page 45) that skin testing is a very safe procedure. It is, however, wise and prudent to ensure that the room has an emergency call system.

Table 3 Equipment required for skin prick testing

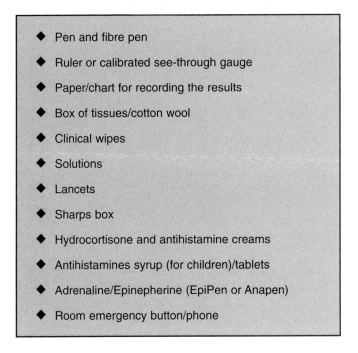

◆ Pen and fibre pen

◆ Ruler or calibrated see-through gauge

◆ Paper/chart for recording the results

◆ Box of tissues/cotton wool

◆ Clinical wipes

◆ Solutions

◆ Lancets

◆ Sharps box

◆ Hydrocortisone and antihistamine creams

◆ Antihistamines syrup (for children)/tablets

◆ Adrenaline/Epinepherine (EpiPen or Anapen)

◆ Room emergency button/phone

Site to be tested

Several authors have investigated the reactivity of the skin of the back and volar surface of the forearms. Some report a similar sensitivity, but only a few have reported on differences in skin reactivity between the different areas. For example it was found that there was a significant difference in skin reactivity between left and right forearm (Taudorf, 1985) and also that differences were found between the back and the volar surface of the forearm when using different needles/lancets (Holgerson, 1985). These variations seem to be accidental, as there were only two significant differences amongst a great number of tested differences in several trials. Thus the choice of the back or the volar surface of the forearm as a test area is of minor importance (Dreborg, 1988).

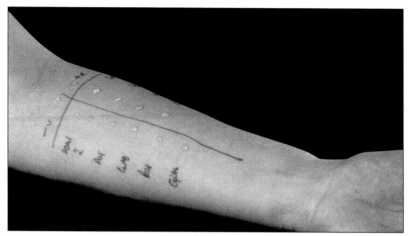

Figure 12 Volar aspect of arm prepared for testing.

Forearm sensitivity to histamine varies two-fold between the elbow and the wrist due to the laxer connective tissue in the paroximal arm, and there are also differences between the flexor and extensor aspects of the forearm (Galant & Maibach, 1973). Skin tests should therefore be grouped together on the volar aspect of the forearm. A guideline is 3 cm down from the elbow and 5 cm up from the wrist. If large numbers of tests are to be performed then the skin of the back provides an extensive area of consistent sensitivity (Frew, 1997).

The basic principle of skin testing is to introduce a small amount of allergen extract into the epidermis. Here, if there are allergen specific IgE molecules on the surface of the cutaneous mast cells, the antigen will cross-link the IgE causing a signal to be passed via Fc_ε receptors to the mast cell cytoplasm. This will trigger degranulation, histamine release and generation of the other mediators, including Leukotrienes. The chemical mediators cause vasodilation and increase vascular permeability, which in turn leads to tissue oedema and the development of a weal. Axon reflexes cause the surrounding skin to flush. This is the basis of the classic weal-and-flare response described by Lewis in 1927 as described on page 6 (Lewis, 1927).

Figure 13

It is usual for the Volar aspect of the patient's arm, (as shown in figures 12 & 13) to be used. Even very young children, invited to play a game, co-operate once they know they can see what is going on. However where there is extensive eczema present then the patient's back, if clear of eczema, is a suitable alternative site. If possible, the negative and positive controls can be performed on the patient's arm in order to show what will happen on their back. The controls can then be repeated on the back.

Prior to skin testing the procedure should be explained to the patient. They should be reassured on any anxieties they may have, and their questions should be answered as precisely as possible in order to obtain verbal consent to proceed with the test. Even very young children have the right to withdraw consent. Children under sixteen should be accompanied by their parent or guardian. It is very useful to ask "are you afraid of needles?" and to show the patient the lancet. It may also be helpful to demonstrate on the patient (without allergens) what a skin prick test feels like. Some children have been known to tell their friends that "they" use razor blades!

It is also useful to ask the patient not to hold their breath whilst being tested.

The author has found that teenage girls are the main group who suffer from needle phobia and who tend to feel faint simply because they have forgotten to breathe whilst the test is being carried out.

The patient should be invited to roll up their sleeve and to place the nearest arm on the table. Children may prefer to kneel on a chair with the arm placed on a pillow on the table. Infants and younger children are best held by their parent or guardian with their back to them, as shown in figures 14-16.

The parent or guardian then tucks the child's arm which is not being tested under their arm which is also extended across the child's chest, reaching to hold the upper part of the child's arm to be tested (see figure 14).

Figure 14 Example of holding control in a young child

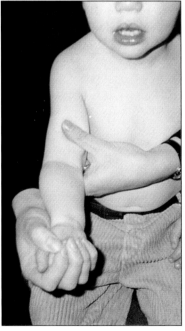

Figure 15 Clearer view of arm for testing

Figure 16 Example of holding control in an older child.

The parent's or guardian's other hand holds the child's hand allowing the forearm to be extended from the elbow so as to facilitate testing, as shown in figures 14 & 15. A slightly different holding control with an older child is shown in figure 16. It is much easier if the child is stripped down to his/her vest, as loose sleeves, even rolled up, can brush the solutions, particularly if the child should raise objections and pull away. It is evident from the pictures that both the child and the parent are comfortable with this form of holding control.

Children who can only be tested on their backs are more comfortable if laid across a firm pillow on a couch or across the parent's lap, back uppermost. This however often requires two adults, particularly for very young children, one supporting the head and arms whilst distracting the child and the other adult keeping the back, bottom and legs from wriggling. This latter position is commonly used in the USA, but it is the author's experience that most children co-operate for 3-4 quick tests on their arm, particularly if they can see what is going on. It is much better to do a few tests, gain the child's confidence and invite him/her back again should further tests be required.

Figures 17-21 show a two year old boy, "Professor" Lewis, happily going

Figure 17 Coding the arm

Figure 18 You can use a rule for measuring

Figure 19 Or gauges

Figure 20 This result looks interesting

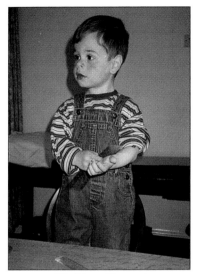

Figure 21 Would you like me to go through this again?

through the procedure himself shortly after being tested and having had his results assessed. This is a very good example of how well young children can cope with skin prick testing and actually demonstrates some understanding of the procedure.

It is not always necessary to clean the site for testing. However, should this be necessary, wash with water or wipe the test site with alcohol prior to testing. The factors determining whether the site should be cleaned are:

1. General cleanliness of the patient.
2. If the patient has used body lotion etc.

The latter can cause a change in the surface tension and may cause the drop of allergen to run or soak up the solution like blotting paper.

However, whatever form of cleansing is carried out, it is important to ensure that the site is thoroughly dry before applying the test solutions.

Procedure

The following sections cover the basic procedure for carrying out the skin prick test and measuring the results. In general, the various items of equipment required and recommended for use are listed in Table 3 (see page 25). The allergens are selected in accordance with the patient's history and are

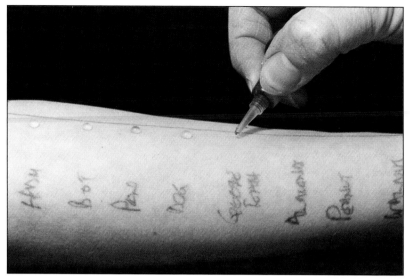

Figure 22 Picture of coded arm and use of solution dropper.

lined up to correspond with the coding on the patient's test site. The test site is coded with a felt tip pen, as shown in figure 22, or with a marker which is provided by some pharmaceutical companies.

The site is marked with a negative (-ve) and positive control (+ve) about 3 cm from the cubital fossa and 5 cm above the wrist. The allergens are coded about 3 cm below each other, going down the arm in 2 columns about 3 cm apart. This is to allow for the test response not to overlap and thus induce strong reactions on other slightly positive or negative responses (see figures 12 and 22). A similar procedure for spacing is applied if using the back. Coding could be the first three letters of the allergen solution or numbers could be used.

The author prefers the first three letters as it seems pointless to label a bottle twice by adding numbers. It helps small children who are unable to read to understand the procedure if, instead of writing, a cat or dog etc. is drawn at the test site (subject to the operator's artistic skills!).

A drop of control solution is placed next to the -ve and +ve coded marks and the allergens are then placed beside each allergen code. The patient should be asked to keep still so that the allergens do not run into each other, although the phenol glycerine in the allergen test solution helps to stop this happening. It is important that the solution dropper does not touch the patient's skin (cross infection, see figure 22). The patient should then be

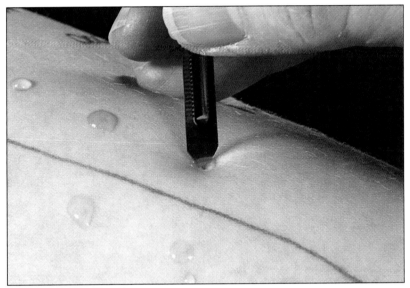

Figure 23 Pricking the skin

shown the lancet again and talked through the procedure. The lancet should be gently but firmly pricked through the centre of the controls and the allergens (as shown in figure 23) and it is then withdrawn straight up. The lancet should be pressed, not jabbed, at 90 degrees to the skin.

The same pressure should be applied each time. The author has found that when testing some very young children, getting them to listen for "a magic click" helps to keep them still and quiet i.e using a form of the modified skin prick test whereby the skin is very slightly raised as the lancet is withdrawn.

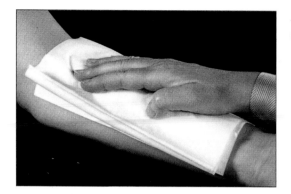

Figure 24 Blotting excess solution

The lancet should be wiped clean with a tissue or cotton wool before the next allergen is pricked. The author usually starts with the negative control and finishes with the positive control, simply because if the positive is pricked first an itching response may start before all the allergens have been pricked and the younger patient may become restless.

Once all the allergen drops have been pricked the excess allergen solutions should then be removed by placing a tissue over the testing site as shown in figure 24. It is of paramount importance that the tissue is not wiped through the arm. The solutions should always be blotted off. If a wiping process is used there is a distinct risk of carrying over the allergens into each other and producing false results. The patient should be asked to roll their sleeve down or put their clothes back on. This helps to keep the arm or back warm whilst waiting for any reactions to develop. The time of the test should be recorded and the allergens selected for testing should be listed on an appropriate record sheet.

Some companies provide numbered tape to place on the forearm or the back at the test site in order to help gauge the correct distance between the allergens. It is the author's view that numbered coding either with a marker pen or tape has limitations, not least from the patient's point of view. They like to know whether it is the cat, dog or whatever that is starting to itch.

Children generally do not like the tape being peeled off and much prefer the tickle of a pen. Patients often ask before being tested whether it will hurt. This is best answered by stating "it is a little uncomfortable and if you are allergic, the site will itch and look as if you have been stung by a stinging nettle". The majority of children can identify with this explanation and as already stated the procedure is well tolerated even by very small children.

Recording the reaction

The intention when skin testing is to introduce a very small volume of extract into the superficial dermis. Where a positive reaction is to develop, the patient will notice itching within 2-3 minutes of testing, followed by erythema and then a weal which expands progressively between 5 and 15 minutes after testing.

The results of the skin test are read as follows. The controls are read about 5-10 minutes after the test and the allergens 15-20 minutes later. The results are read by measuring the size of a weal in response to the allergen. The measuring can be achieved by using a ruler and the diameter of the weal is measured as shown in figure 25.

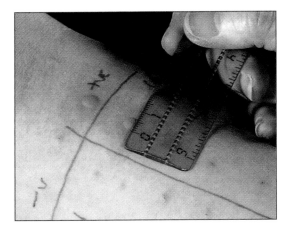

Figure 25 Measuring diameter of weal

In Europe the weal response is considered the most relevant measure of skin reactivity. In some patients reactions take a little longer to develop, therefore the test sites should be reinspected at 25-30 minutes and the largest reaction recorded.

To obtain a permanent record, the contours of the weal and erythema can be outlined with a fine filter tip pen or ball point pen and the contours transferred by means of translucent tape to a record sheet. In routine clinical practice, the mean diameter of the weal is usually sufficient (Malling, 1993) as in figure 25. A transparent ruler is adequate to use for measurement however some companies do provide gauges as shown in figure 26. The positive (histamine) control is also measured and this response is maximal after 10 minutes. Where a weal is elicited to the negative control, it is customary to subtract this value from the measurements of the other weals, although it has been pointed out that this practice has not been formally validated (Frew,1997).

However in North America most allergists regard a weal which is 3 to 5 mm larger in size than the negative control to be a positive skin test result.

If all tests including the negative control give moderate or large weals it is best to use alternative means of diagnosis i.e. serological tests (Frew, 1997).

In an EAACI (European Academy of Allergy & Clinical Immunology) Position Paper, it is pointed out that most studies about skin prick testing have used only the weal and not the erythema reaction for evaluation of the response. The weal induced by the trauma of the needle/lancet and the negative control solution is often zero, but may amount to 2.5 mm in diameter (5 mm^2) in single tests in patients without otherwise demonstrable dermatographism, therefore weals < 3 mm in diameter should be regarded as negative. However, when repeated negative controls do not show a lower response, then the cut off limit can be lowered. Thus, without special precautions, only weals ≥ 3 mm in diameter should be regarded as positive (Dreborg, 1989).

In another EAACI Paper it is recommended that the weal area is the

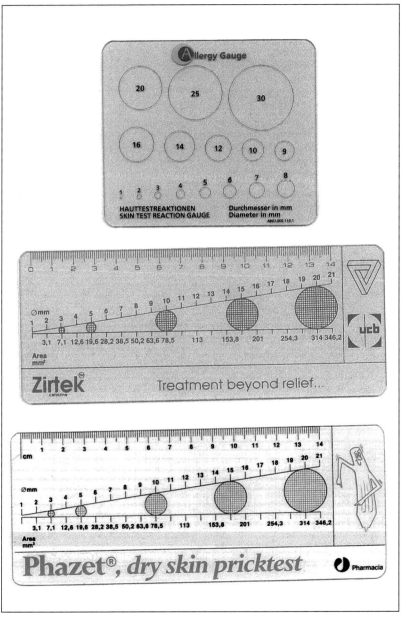

Figure 26 Examples of rulers & gauges

indicator most used to evaluate skin prick tests, and areas greater than 7 mm^2 (Diameter > 3 mm) are accepted as positive. Skin sensitivity is often expressed as the allergen concentration eliciting a weal reaction equivalent to that of histamine, as either end point or mid-point titration (Malling, 1985). However Malling goes on to say that the best expression of skin sensitivity has not been agreed: both the histamine-equivalent technique and the mid-point technique need further investigation. When evaluating changes in skin sensitivity by means of skin testing it is not appropriate to compare the weal size induced by histamine with the weal induced by another reference substance (Basomba, 1993).

A skin prick test reaction is considered to be positive when the mean weal diameter is > 3 mm [area > 7 mm^2], (Haahtel, 1993). This is called the detection limit or cut-off limit of the method. In some studies a cut-off limit of > 2 mm [Area 3 mm^2] has been used and Haahtel further reiterates that the background response (i.e. the weal response to diluent / negative control) should be carefully documented. The difference between using a 2 mm and a 3 mm diameter cut-off limit is equivalent to a 10 fold difference in skin sensitivity.

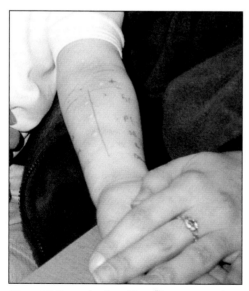

Figure 27 Example of positive skin test

Patients diagnosed as skin test positive at 3 mm usually retain their sensitivity over time, whereas those diagnosed on a 2 mm cut-off often oscillate between positivity and negativity. This switching between categories reflects the inherent variability of the tests as well as the relatively lower concentrations of specific IgE at a true test diameter of

2 mm (Frew, 1997). It is not clear from the literature whether this criteria applies equally to infants, children and adults.

Skin weals of 2 mm and 3 mm are not clinically important in children aged 12-14 years, as different weal sizes may be appropriate for defining atopy at different ages because the condition appears to develop during childhood and increase in severity until adulthood (Peat & Woodcock, 1991). The following cut-off points are used by the author: 2 mm response for children of 4 years and under and 3 mm greater than the negative control for older children and adults.

It is also the author's experience that the histamine response in the majority of patients tested (approx. 4,500), which included children, produced on average a weal of 5 mm, and that most allergen responses were between 3 mm to 5 mm. Therefore if the criteria for assessing the results is to compare the allergen response with the histamine, as some manufacturers advocate, then most allergen results would need to be a minimum of 9 mm.

This could effectively mean a high percentage of patients would be regarded as non-atopic and possibly may not receive the appropriate treatment. Furthermore, it has been found that there is no consistent relation between the allergen weal diameter and the histamine weal diameter, and it has been concluded that one should not adjust allergen weal to histamine weal (Chinn, 1996).

If after testing the patient experiences discomfort, then an antihistamine (tablet or syrup) can be given or a cream such as antihistamine or hydrocortisone 1% can be applied to the tested site. It is normal to advise the patient to wash the test site once the allergen responses have disappeared. The positive reactions usually subside within the hour, although occasionally large responses may persist for 24 hours.

There is a possibility that a late reaction can occur 5-6 hours after skin testing, peaking in 6-12 hours, manifesting as indurated skin (Dolovich, 1973).

Interpreting the results

The value of skin tests, like that of any diagnostic procedure, depends on the knowledge of the interpreter. To be informative the tests must relate to the patient's clinical history. The selection of allergens and the administration of the tests require experience and knowledge. It is important to be aware of the reasons for false-positive and false-negative results in order to evaluate the test properly.

False – negative results

In addition to those points discussed on factors influencing the results on page 8, the refractory period needs to be considered. Soon after a systemic reaction to an allergen such as insect venom, penicillin, or food, the patient enters a refractory period during which a skin test reaction to that substance may be negative. The reason is that specific IgE is consumed by the severe allergic reaction, and a three to four week period is needed for the allergic antibody to build back up to its prereaction levels. Therefore if a patient has a systemic reaction to an allergen, it is best to wait four full weeks before performing skin tests (Fireman & Slavin,1991).

As has already been pointed out, whenever a skin test is performed histamine should be included as a positive control. If the histamine skin test result is negative, this shows that the patient has taken anti-histamines or other treatments previously referred to, and in consequence the treatment is blocking the histamine response and that of the allergens. Therefore the patient will have to be retested at another time.

False – positive results

In the clinical setting patients selected for skin prick testing may present with symptoms which are not necessarily associated with a specific allergen. For example, patients may show a positive skin test response to cat or dog even though there is no cat or dog in the family home, work place or school, or indeed may not develop any symptoms on visiting places where these animals are present. The positive skin test response demonstrates that the patient has IgE antibodies but their body is coping and that there is no breakdown i.e. development of symptoms. However this false positive skin test response could be predictive of future sensitivity with symptom development, and in this case it might be helpful to advise the patient not to have domestic pets.

This view is supported by the following statement: "In practice, a positive skin test for one allergen apparently unrelated to history should be considered to be a potential trigger of symptoms in particular situations of exposure" (Pastorello, 1993).

A positive test in a symptom-free subject is evidence of latent allergy or subclinical allergy. A positive pollen test in an asymptomatic subject indicates a 10-fold increase in the risk of developing seasonal rhinitis (Mygind, 1996). This phenomenon was described in the 1940s by Carl Juhlin-Dannfeldt, and more recently by Horak. Latent allergy in children is most often predictive for the development of clinical allergy (Dreborg, 1989).

For a symptomatic patient, exposure to an allergen causing a positive skin test will usually be of clinical significance. However a skin test can remain positive long after (years in some cases) the patient has ceased to have any symptoms. In the elderly, a positive test without symptoms more often indicates an outgrown allergy (Dreborg,1989).

On the other hand patients may not give a clear history if they are exposed to low doses of allergen, or if they are only slightly sensitive and are continuously exposed to high concentrations of allergens. In such cases the combination of continuous symptoms and continuous allergen exposure is usually taken to indicate relevant sensitisation (Pastorello, 1993).

Unusual responses to skin prick tests

Pseudopodia

Most skin test responses are circular weal responses but occasionally "legs" or other irregular extensions are seen, as shown in figure 28. This is simply local gravitation to other mast cells. The "legs" or extensions are not usually taken into account when measuring the weal.

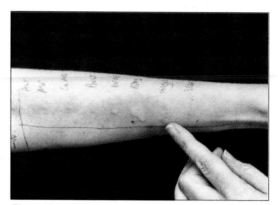

Figure 28 An example of pseudopodia

Satellite response

This is a rare response, which has been witnessed by the author when testing a 2 year old child. The test was carried out on her back, but the area on the back where the skin prick test was performed did not elicit a response. However, it was evident that satellite responses 3 & 5 cm distant from the prick test did occur, with weal responses of 3 mm and 5 mm (see figure 29).

The satellite response is another example of allergen gravitation to mast cells where the site chosen for testing was absent of mast cells.

Late Phase Responses

Allergic or hypersensitive reactions have been classified into four categories depending on the timing of the reaction. For example, symptoms which occur within minutes of the allergen exposure are known as *immediate* reactions. Symptoms which occur after some hours are called *late* reactions and after some days are called *delayed* reactions. These hypersensitivity reactions are

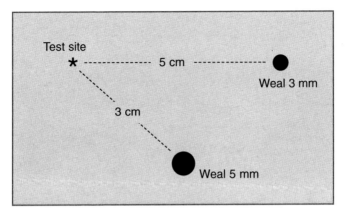

Figure 29 Satellite Response

classified as Type I-IV responses (Coombs & Gell, 1975) which tend to follow known clinical disease patterns. This is a very simplified explanation of the reactions which generally act in concert rather than in isolation (Mygind, 1996). The same responses can occur with skin prick testing.

The immediate response to skin prick testing is seen within 15-30 minutes of the challenge which in essence is mimicking, for example, the immediate response as seen in the hay-fever sufferer who may sneeze immediately on exposure to grasses.

In a study reporting on late phase skin (SPT) reactions in seven bakers and seven control subjects to malted wheat, and not preceded by an immediate reaction, it was found that the late SPT reactions started at about 6-10 hours after the test and remained for approximately a further 12 hours. In all but one subject, the initial result when the SPT was read after 15 minutes was negative. At retest after 2 months, the late reactions were reproduced in all bakers and all controls. The late reactions had diameters of 1-20 mm and were erythmatous and oedematous, but there was no visible epidermal damage and the size of the reactions in each subject was similar on the left and right arm. The clinical observations were investigated by immunohisto-chemical methods (Meding, 1998). The authors concluded that the late skin reactions observed were probably more of an irritant or toxic nature than of an immune-mediated nature. However it has been shown that late reactions may occur as well as or instead of the immediate response (Jackson, 1988).

Sometimes a more ill-defined response, usually a soft swelling, may occur at the site from 8-24 hours after the test. It is believed that this probably represents immune-complex deposition in a Type III reaction. However its clinical significance is often unclear, and it may sometimes be correlated with symptoms of delayed onset after allergen exposure or with a biphasic response in bronchial challenge testing. In clinical practice, demonstration of late-phase reactions is considered to be of special significance in the patho-genesis of allergic tissue responses and for assessing the influence of different types of therapy, e.g. steroids, immunology and anti-allergic drugs (Holgate & Church, 1993).

The main disorders in which Type III reaction (Arthus) is recognised to be clinically relevant are respiratory allergic disorders such as allergic Bronchopulmonary Aspergillosis, in which both reagins and precipitins are a feature, and extrinsic allergic alveolitis such as bird-fanciers lung. It is com-mon for these patients to report the appearance of a second much larger swelling some hours after immediate wealing reactions have subsided. The Type I reaction, on which the evolution of the Type III reaction appears to depend, is sufficient to show the presence of allergy to Aspergillus fumigatus (Pepys, 1975).

Most of these late responses resolve spontaneously within 24 hours, and the relationship between IgE dependent late cutaneous reactions and the Arthus-type skin response is unclear. It is considered that more studies are needed to address the clinical significance of this so called "latent allergy" (Hattevig,1987). Finally, it is suggested that the late phase response (LPR) almost never appears without an immediate reaction (Dreborg, 1989). If any late or delayed responses are anticipated, the appropriate patients should be advised and given reassurance that the responses will resolve.

CHAPTER FOUR

Allergy
and the Patient

The patient's main question

Patients often ask "is the size of the weal an indicator of whether I have mild, moderate or severe allergic symptoms?". Skin test reactivity to common allergens is considered to be indicative of the subject's general tendency to develop immediate Type I reactions. The tests are used as an indicator of a subject's "Atopic disposition". Present data indicate a close and quantitative relationship between the frequency of "allergic" respiratory problems ("asthma" and "allergic rhinitis") and the severity of allergy skin-prick test reactions. Increasingly large reactions are associated with increasing prevalencies of allergic disease (Burrows, 1976). The larger the skin reaction the higher the risk of allergic symptoms (Mygind, 1996).

In testing for 13 common allergens it was reported that children with one or more positive skin test weals ≥ 3 mm had significantly more recent wheeze, hay-fever, eczema and bronchial hyperresponsiveness than children with smaller weals (Peat and Woodcock, 1991). Therefore a large skin test response must not be equated as "very allergic"; the history gives more information than any provocation test (Frankland, 1985). In conclusion the test itself does not indicate the severity or otherwise of the allergic symptoms themselves.

Safety of skin prick testing

Skin prick testing to common aeroallergens is regarded as a completely safe procedure. There is, however, a hypothetical risk associated with giving allergens to which the patient is sensitive by what ever route, so it is sensible to have adrenaline available for immediate use. However, one has to balance this advice with the fact that the sufferer will undoubtedly have inhaled more allergen than the amount of allergen that is likely to be used to penetrate the skin on prick testing (see page 19).

The diagnosis for food allergy is difficult and food extracts for skin testing are not well characterised. Particular caution should be used when interpreting skin tests to foods. Only a fraction of patients with positive tests will react during food challenge, which suggests that many who react have lost their clinical sensitivity (Mygind, 1996). Initially it was recognised that skin prick testing was rarely used to confirm food hypersensitivity due to a small risk of anaphylaxis. However in a review of children (aged 6 months to 16 years) with suspected allergy over an 18 month period, 687 patients were skin prick tested using commercially available extracts. All the children had skin prick tests to one or several allergenic foods (cow's milk, soya-bean, egg white, cod fish, wheat flour, peanut and tree nuts) as well as aeroallergens. The procedure was carried out in the paediatric outpatient department. 421 children (61%) had confirmed immediate food hypersensitivity, and this included children with a history of anaphylaxis and respiratory problems (34%). Nine children (1.3%) suffered adverse reactions i.e. eight vaso-vagal episodes and one child with cow's milk allergy had allergic complications to the test, i.e. within three minutes he developed a distal urticarial lesion on his forehead, but remained otherwise well. No respiratory symptoms were observed in any of the children tested.

The authors concluded that though their cohort was small it did comprise a high risk population with a history of severe allergic reactions to foods, but they believed that skin prick testing is a safe method to confirm food allergy in children (Gaughan, 1998).

Another study concluded that skin prick testing confirmed the test's usefulness as a supportive and safe test for excluding peanut allergy (Hourihane, 1996).

However, in another study it was reported that an anaphylactic reaction occurred in a 57 year old man after prick by prick testing with fresh fruit, and in a 29 year old man after skin prick testing with some species of fish. The latter's history showed that he had an exquisite sensitivity to fish, as did his father and grandfather. Twenty minutes after the test the patient presented with the following symptoms: itchy throat; severe dyspnoea; and collapse. He improved rapidly on subcutaneous Epinepherine, intravenous steroids and intramuscular antihistamines. The batch of tests included 9 other common foods and 9 aeroallergens all of which were negative. The authors concluded that skin prick testing is very useful and safe in the diagnosis of food allergy, but it should be borne in mind that the allergenic potency of many commercial extracts is not well known (Novembre, 1995).

In a further study of 62 food allergic patients, aged between 11 months to 53 years, it was concluded that "skin prick tests were completely safe and did not cause any systemic reactions... in keeping with our experience of skin tests in anaphylaxis from other causes" (Ewan, 1990).

Skin prick tests are safe and may easily be performed in general practice (Nolan, 1999). However it is not a recommended practice unless the professional has the appropriate experience and skills. It should also be a golden rule in general practice not to skin test patients with a proven history of anaphylaxis to foods. In highly sensitive patients, especially patients with a history of anaphylaxis, it is recommended that weaker concentrations of the solutions should be used and only a minimal number of tests carried out at one session so as to minimise the risk of systemic reaction.

The test sites should be examined 12-24 hours later because of the possibility of a late phase component of Type I reaction, although this has rarely been observed in controlled studies (Sampson, 1991).

CHAPTER FIVE

Summary

The current methods of skin testing vary among regions and also among medical specialists. At present the skin prick test method using a lancet with 1 mm tip is the method of choice for routine diagnosis, especially among paediatricians. In contrast to results obtained by laboratory methods, skin prick test results are often presented without giving details of the potency of the allergen preparation used, the method of testing or the reproducibility in the hands of the investigator (Dreborg and Frew, 1993). It is their hope that the recommendations within their position paper on the performance, evaluation and use of skin tests in diagnosis, standardisation and epidemiologic studies will be followed by European allergologists.

Whilst the overall ambition is to strive to meet these European standards, they can only be achieved if the standards involved in the methods of testing and reproducibility are addressed. This will only come about by the doctors and nurses ensuring that they receive comprehensive and quality training together with the required clinical experience. In addition it will require the manufacturers of the skin prick test solutions to achieve agreed standardisation methods and potency levels.

Skin testing should not be a rushed procedure with allergens selected at random. Gone should be the days when patients were lined up and skin tested automatically for whatever the investigator's kit contained. It is certainly not a procedure just to be "got through". The real value of any test, including skin prick testing, lies in its contribution to patient management (Ollier & Davies, 1989). Also, it must be emphasised again that skin prick testing should only be carried out following a clear and precise history.

The value of the test depends on the knowledge of the interpreter and their experience. Patients have a right to know what is the cause of their symptoms and what they are allergic to in order that they can make an educated choice: whether to implement avoidance measures, change their treatment or indeed whether to take their treatment, and ultimately to care for themselves. Seeing the results of the skin prick test is and should be meaningful and helpful to both the patient and the professional.

APPENDIX 1: ALLERGENS

Introduction

Allergens for skin prick testing should be selected according to the patient's history. It is important to consider the home, work and school environment, and also individual and family hobbies. (Please see the Allergy Assessment Questionnaires in Appendix 2.)

Selection of outdoor allergens will depend upon local prevalences. The allergen categories are outlined below with brief comments on the most common allergens.

Animals

Literature shows that recorded allergies exist to 363 different species, which includes the following:

Invertebrates

Classes		Examples
Annelida	-	Earthworms, leeches, and marine worms
Arachnid	-	Mites and ticks
Briozoa	-	Moss animals
Cnidaria	-	Corals, sea anemones, and jelly fish
Crustacea	-	Craw fish, crabs, shrimp, prawn, lobster
Echinodermata	-	Sea urchin
Hymonoptera	-	Bees, wasps and ants
Insects	-	Mayfly, mosquitoes, fruit fly, midges, lice, cockroach and fleas
Molluscs	-	Mussels, oysters, scallops, clams, cockles.
Porifera	-	Sponges.
Platyhelminthes	-	Parasites.

Vertebrates

Classes

Mammals	Fishes
Birds	Reptiles
Amphibians	

The most common vertebrates in regard to allergy are:-

Mammals of the Carnivora Order

Cat	*Felis domesticus*
Dog	*Canis familiaris*

Cat *Felis domesticus*

The most important allergen from the domestic cat is the major allergen *Fel d* I, which is found in cat saliva and lachrymal fluid. *Fel d* I is closely associated with Kallikrein (Kininogenase) from cat skin (Berrens, 1990). It is understood that the major cat allergen is present in the skin (probably as excretion of the sweat glands), not in the saliva, as generally assumed. (A similar close identity is found in dogs, mice and rats). A study of the distribution of *Fel d* I in cat fur and skin with immunohistochemical procedures found that it was 10 fold higher at the root than the tip (Charpin, 1991). The allergen is produced by the sebaceous glands. *Fel d* I and other minor cat allergens are very common and are present in the dust of most houses, even in homes where such animals have never been kept.

Studies show that cat allergen is widely distributed on wall surfaces (Wood, 1992) and detectable concentrations of *Fel d* I in both mattresses and living room floor dust (Egmar, 1993). Aggressive cleaning, removal of soft furnishings and improved ventilation can reduce levels of airborne cat allergen (Luczynska, 1988). It has also been demonstrated that sequential monthly washing markedly reduces *Fel d* I production (Glinert, 1990).

Sera of patients allergic to animal dander in connection to other allergens contained a high frequency of "mite allergy" combined with "cat allergy"; investigations by RAST inhibition and immunoblot revealed that in fact there is a common allergen between house dust mite and cat dander that is relevant in 30% of patients allergic to cats (Kalveram, 1993).

Dog *Canis familiaris*

Dogs are the most popular pets in the world. While some animals seem to be more tolerable than others there are not any dogs, cats or furry animals which do not cause allergic responses. It makes no difference whether an animal has short hair, long hair or how much it sheds.

As dogs progress from birth to old age, a notable change occurs in the quantity of dander and scale produced. Puppies have very supple skins and they shed very little dander, causing relatively few problems, even for animal allergic persons. Ageing animals lose their suppleness and then shed much more profusely [There is a dramatic difference in an animal at 2 months and one at two years, (Perez-Santos,1995).] Interestingly, the dog is the only subhuman species which suffers from clearly defined atopic disease such as hay-fever like signs (Halliwell, 1978). In 1990, the important dog allergen *Can f* I (AG13), a relatively stable molecule which stays in dust for extended periods of time, was purified (Schou, 1990). In 1991 a major and minor allergen from dog extract: *Can f* I (AG 13) was purified. The major allergen is found in dog saliva to which most dog-allergic patients react (70%) and dog allergen 2, the minor allergen to which about 23% of dog-allergic patients react. It was found that dog saliva was a strong allergen source. Dog urine and faeces contain very little of the allergens (de Groot, 1991).

Contrary to popular belief of many dog-allergic individuals, breed specific allergens have never been found (Lindgren, 1988). The variations in allergic activity to individual canine breeds appear to be largely related to difference in the relative concentrations of the shared allergens (Knysak, 1989).

However there are a few breeds, including cocker spaniels, that are prone to Seborrhoea and shed far more dander than others, their epidermal turnover being approximately every 3 to 5 days instead of the normal 21 days.

The treatment of choice in hypersensitivity to animal dander is strict elimination, but most of the time this is difficult to achieve, especially when the animal involved is a cat or dog. This is often due to emotional reasons, or because indirect exposure to pets among school mates, friends, family and in the neighbourhood is responsible for a considerable spread of the allergens.

Perissodactyla	**Order**
Horse	*Equus caballus*

Horses are "ungulates" which is a general term given to all these groups of mammals which have substituted hooves for claws during their evolution. There are, perhaps, as many as 170 distinctive breeds and types of horse throughout the world. Among the domestic horses it seems that the only pure breed is the Arab (Perez-Santos, 1995).

Allergy to horses may be elicited by injections of horse serum, by inhalation of horse dander and hair and by ingesting horse meat (which can induce urticaria and gastro-intestinal disturbances). Considerable interest has also been shown to horse allergen extracts due to the severe allergic reactions or deaths experienced by some horse-sensitive asthmatics on receiving their first injection of therapeutic horse serum.

The presence of the living animal is not essential for the induction of an attack. Symptoms may be induced by the allergen being on the clothes of the horse rider, or even small quantities of dust from horse-hair mattresses. Evaluation of the frequency and type of allergic diseases in 114 occupational riding centre workers exposed to horse danders (stablemen, trainers, jockeys and others) showed that there was a high frequency (11.4%) in the whole group with at least partial sensitisation to horse dander. The main symptoms were rhinitis, conjunctivitis and asthma (Muscato, 1990).

Horse sera are used in medical prophylaxis and therapy in infectious diseases or intoxications and also for biological immunosupression with antilymphocite globulin. The risk of severe allergic reactions exists either as an immediate type anaphylaxis or as serum sickness.

It has been found that repeated intracutaneous injections of any product diluted in horse serum produced no reaction initially. However, after two or more injections a delayed reaction appeared, followed still later by both immediate and delayed reactions, and finally the immediate reaction alone. A study of the incidence of horse serum protein allergy concluded that careful immunologic testing of every patient who is to receive therapy is indicated (Ring, 1997). Commercial allergen extracts to be used in diagnosis and immunotherapy should include horse dander, horse hair and skin scrapings in the starting material for the preparation of extracts. Otherwise, allergens which may be of importance (Glycoprotein and horse serum) for some patients will be missed (Fjeldsgaard, 1993).

Artiodactya   **Order**

Cow	*Bos taurus*
Sheep	*Ovis aries*
Pig	*Sus scrofa*

Bird Class

Canary	Parrot
Hen	Pigeon
Turkey	Duck
Budgerigar	Goose

Allergenicity of feather extracts is due mainly to contamination with mites. Allergy to bird droppings occurs in individuals having close contact within poorly ventilated rooms. It is common among those keeping pigeons and budgerigars but uncommon in poultry breeders. An IgE antibody response results in asthma, while an IgG antibody response to bird antigens is a common cause of extrinsic allergic alveolitis.

Rodentia	Order
Mouse	*Mus musculus*
Rat	*Rattus rattus*
Hamster	*Mesocricetus auratus*
Gerbil	*Meriones unguiculatus*
Guinea pig	*Sciurus spp*

Rodents

Rodents such as mice, rats, guinea pigs and hamsters are widely used in medical research and also as household pets. They are potent allergen sources and constitute an increasing health problem (Mygind, 1996). In these animals urine is the most potent allergen source. Male rodents have permanent proteinuria and often spray their urine rather than just depositing it. As many as 20% of those who are occupationally exposed to these animals become sensitised. Symptoms usually develop within the first year of exposure and atopic subjects, especially those allergic to other mammals, have an increased risk of developing asthma (Mygind, 1996).

Lagomorpha	Order
Rabbit	*Oryctolagus cuniculus*

Phyllum Pisces-Fish	Order
Codfish	*Gadus morhua*
Hake	*Merluccius merluccius*
Anchovy	*Engraulis encrasiolus*
Herring	*Sardina pilchardus*
Salmon	*Salmo salar*
Trout	*S. trutta*
Sole	*Solea vulgaris*
Mackerel	*Scomber scombrus*
Tuna	*Thunnus thynnus*

Anisomyaria **Order**

Mussels *Mytilus edulus*
Scallop *Pecten maxmus*
Oysters *Crassosterea virginica*

Subphylum Crustacea

Crabs
Shrimps/prawn

The commonest invertebrates in regard to allergy:

Insect class (Roaches)

Midges
Mosquitoes
Beetles

Hymenoptera

Bees
Wasps
Ants

Arachnida class – Mites

The Arachnids are predators of external parasites. They have six pairs of jointed appendages, the first for feeding by piercing their prey or host and sucking out its bodily fluids. The second pair act as sensory organs that detect touch and chemicals and help to hold the food in place while an arachnid is eating. The other four pairs are walking legs. There are 30,000 species of arachnids and they are divided into 10 actual living orders. The commonly known being:

Scorpions *Scorpionida*
Spiders *Araneae*
Mites and ticks *Acarina*

Some members of these families have been cited as a cause of allergy. The most well known and common cause of allergy are those from the Acarina order (which includes many families) the commonest being the Pyroglyphidae family – house dust mite. Mites associated with the nests of birds or mammals and free-living mites are regularly found in house dust in large parts of the world.

The most prevalent from this family are *Dermatophagoides farinae*, known as the American house dust mite, and *Dermatophagoides pteronyssinus*, known as the European house dust mite. In rare instances members of the genus *Dermatophagoides* have been recovered from human sputum and urine (Perez-Santos, 1995).

D. farinae

It is probably one of the least ecologically specialised members of this family, which have been found in house dust, animal skin, nests, stored food, flour, rats, mice, and scalp dermatitis of humans.

D. pteronyssinus

It is usually found in house dust, which as well as providing a habitat for the mites, also contains their food source, namely shed human skin scales, which become colonised by microfungi, yeasts and bacteria. In a few cases it has been collected from mammals, birds and their nests.

Mites belonging to the genus dermatophagoides have been shown to be the most important allergenic constituents of house dust. The life of a mite is short – approximately 120 days – during which time the females each produce 40 - 80 eggs. The life cycle, the duration of which is dependent on temperature, consists of five stages: egg – larva – protonyph – tritonymph – adult. The average size of mites (depending on the species) is about 350 µm in length and 400 μm in width. The males are smaller than the females. The temperature for mite development ranges from 25°C to 28°C, maximal and minimal lethal temperatures being 60°C and –15°C; mites may survive just a few hours at those temperatures. Humidity is usually the decisive limiting factor for mite growth. Relative humidity for the house dust mite to grow ranges from 45% to 90%.

Therefore the optimum temperatures and relative humidity for house dust mite to grow is 25°C to 28°C and 75%. Most allergens provided by the house dust mite are enzymes, which have been found in extracts enriched with mite faecal pellets, suggesting they are associated with digestion (Colloff, 1992). House dust mites are poikilothermic, i.e. they cannot regulate internal body temperature or metabolic rate, so egg production and population growth undergo a decline at low temperatures.

Control of mites and their allergens

Mite and allergen control in homes of patients with mite sensitivities must be directed towards the sites that contain most respirable allergens. These sites depend on individual domestic habits and practices. It should be aimed at areas in the house where people spend most of their time and where allergen exposure is heaviest. The overall important sites are mattresses and bedding, because most people are in contact with them for about 8 hours a day. Bedroom carpets, living room carpets and upholstered furniture are also very important sites, especially for infants who may spend at least as much time per day in contact with these items as with bedding.

Several products are available on the market which are aimed at reducing exposure to allergens of mites and pets. Their efficacy has been proved only in laboratory cultures, and in order to have the same efficacy on natural populations the toxicity is thought to be too high to be used safely in the house (Perez-Santos, 1995). Indeed this is believed to be a matter of major public concern (Colloff, 1992).

Hymenoptera Venom – Bee & Wasp

The term "Hymenoptera" is Greek and means "membrane and wing". Bees are from the Apidae family and wasps and hornets come from the Vespitae family. As a natural response to hymenoptera stings the human immunological system produces both specific IgE and IgG antibodies. IgG antibody production occurs slightly later than the IgE production which persists for several years, whereas IgG can be observed in patients for weeks and months after a sting. IgG antibodies are regarded as "blocking antibodies" and are associated with protection against future stings, but it has never been proven in spite of high titers of this antibody being found in bee-keepers who are immune to bee stings and in patients treated with bee and/or wasp immunotherapy. Both IgE and IgG antibody serum levels are time-dependent (Perez-Santos, 1995)

Reactions to Apidae and/or Vespids stings can be divided into the following categories (Evans & Summers, 1986):

Non Immunological
Toxic	-	local
	-	systemic

Immunological
	-	Large local reactions
	-	Anaphylaxis
	-	Serum sickness

Unknown mechanism
	-	Nephrosis
	-	Vasculitis
	-	Encephalopathy
	-	Neuritis

If the reaction is non immunological, it will usually subside within 48 hours. The weal around the stinging site is less than 10 cm in diameter. Usually there is no systemic reaction and no production of IgE or IgG antibodies.

This response is believed to be due to toxic and inflammatory components present in the venom.

In immunological responses the weal is often greater than 10 cm in diameter and persists for more than 48 hours, with other symptoms such as urticaria, angio-oedema, wheezing and stridor and in severe cases anaphylaxis.

In unknown mechanisms the most usual reactions are vasculitis, nephrosis, neuritis and encephalopathy. The first two occur one or two days after multiple stings. Neurologic and vascular symptoms may be observed several days after the sting and may progress over long periods of time. The pathogenesis is unknown and immunotherapy is contra-indicated.

It is a major rule that any reaction remote from the sting is allergic. In the very rare case of multiple stings it is possible that the remote reaction is a direct effect of toxins. However it has been estimated that 500 stings will deliver a lethal dose of venom (Mygind, 1996).

Skin prick testing for Hymenoptera allergy should only be carried out in hospitals.

Microfungi (Moulds)

Microfungi are microscopic plants lacking chlorophyll. They are dependent on plant or animal material for nourishment, are ubiquitous and play an important ecological role converting waste organic matter to humus. They are saprophytic on dead matter, parasitic on plants and occasionally invasive in humans.

Moulds can survive unfavourable conditions by producing vast numbers of spores which outnumber the pollen grains in the air. While the larger pollen grains (20-30 µm) mainly cause conjunctivitis and rhinitis, the major symptom of allergy to the smaller mould spores (2-5 µm) is asthma (Mygind, 1996).

The common mould species are Alternaria alternata, Aspergillus fumigatus, Cladosporium herbarum, Mucor and Penicillium. These are regarded as the most important causes of mould allergy with the frequency to mould allergy, being higher in children than adults.

The moulds can be found indoors and outdoors, with the spore count being lower indoors. Humidity is the determining factor for growth, which can be immense in badly constructed houses. Moulds can grow in humidifiers, particularly those used in air conditioning systems which are then disseminated through a building. Outdoors, wet weather encourages mould growth and sunny windy weather promotes spore release. Snow reduces mould and spores considerably. The comparison of species reveals that the conditions influencing the release of species is highly variable but can be extremely specific for a given species e.g. *Didymella extalis* and basidiospores, which release spores at night after rain and may be the cause of increased asthma after thunderstorms (Holgate & Church, 1993). The Basiomycotina spp (mushrooms, puff balls, rusts, smuts and bracket fungi) are also thought to represent significant allergen sources. Both groups use airborne dispersal and are often produced in very large quantities. Spore counts for Cladosporium and Alternaria are highest in late summer (one of the commonest causes for late seasonal asthma). The spore counts are high in areas of decaying plant material, not least compost heaps, and are carried for many miles.

For many generations, workers involved in occupations within the bread, cheese, beer and wine manufacturing industries have been exposed to microfungi. In latter years this has included places of work involving antibiotic, enzyme and steroid manufacture. Certainly, great care needs to be taken during the production of purified mould extracts.

There are hundreds of different species and skin test reactions to mould extracts are not always convincingly positive, thus making the diagnosis of mould allergy difficult. Some of the saprophytic moulds can occasionally be pathogens, with moulds eliciting different immune responses and different diseases, e.g. massive exposure to moulds growing in the airway can evoke IgE and an IgG response in Bronchopulmonary Aspergillosis; mould antigens in organic dust can cause IgG responses in non-atopic persons such as allergic alveolitis and may account for 10-20% of allergic disease (Mygind, 1996).

Pollen

This is the most common cause of allergy which may account for 10-20% of allergic diseases in the community, the most well known being hay-fever (seasonal rhinitis)

A pollen grain is the male sexual cell essential for reproduction of seed plants. The grain can be transferred by insects or wind from one plant to another.

Insect-pollinated plants produce few heavy pollen grains which stick to the legs of insects, therefore only closely sniffing the plant will result in allergic symptoms.

Pollen grains from individual species vary in size, ranging from 5 to 200 μm. However in windborne (Anemophlous) pollen the size and range varies from 17-58 μm. The most relevant pollens are found in grasses, weeds, and trees (see figures 30 & 31). In the UK and Europe pollen from various grasses, including the crested dog's tail, fescue, foxtail, meadow rye, timothy, cocksfoot and brome, are common causes of symptoms.

The weather affects the pollen count. Pollen is only released in large quantities on warm sunny days. For grasses in the UK the peak of the "pollen season" occurs during June and July. The pollen is released in the morning, but as the air heats up it is carried high into the air during the middle of the day, descending again as the air cools in the late afternoon. The highest pollen counts usually occur, therefore, in mid-morning and late afternoon. Cities stay hotter longer so the pollen count often stays high well into the evening, whereas it falls earlier in rural areas. Heavy rain usually results in a dramatic fall in the pollen count (Jackson, 1988).

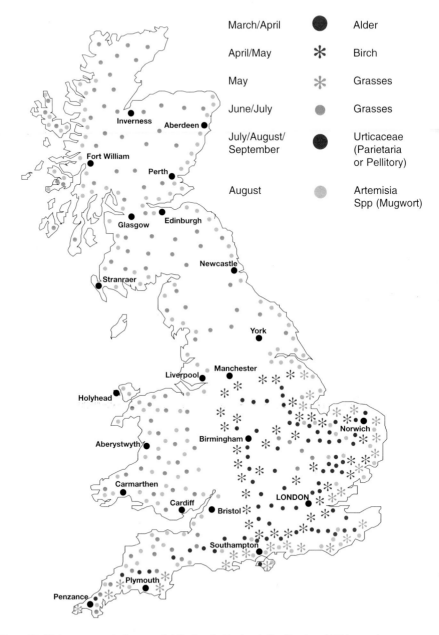

Figure 30 Major seasonal allergen distribution in England, Scotland and Wales

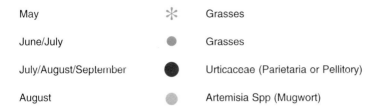

May	✳	Grasses
June/July	⬤	Grasses
July/August/September	⬤	Urticaceae (Parietaria or Pellitory)
August	⬤	Artemisia Spp (Mugwort)

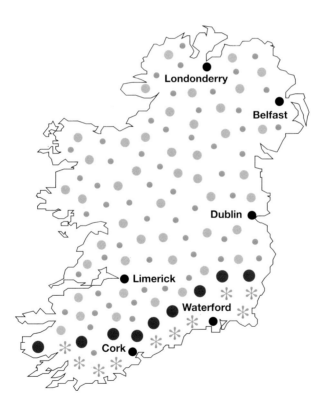

Figure 31 Major seasonal allergen distribution in Ireland

The pollen implicated in causing symptoms are found in grasses, trees and weeds.

Grasses

Bermuda	*Cynodon dactylon*
Brome	*Bromus Spp*
Orchard grasses	*Dactylis glomerata*
Rye	*Lolium perenne*
Common reed	*Phragmites communis*
Timothy	*Phleum pratense*
Meadow fescue	*Festuca pratensis*
Cocksfoot	*Dactylus glomerata*
Meadow grass	*Poa spp*

Tree pollen

Alder	*Alnus glutinosa*
Birch	*Betula verrucosa*
Hazel	*Corylus avelana*
Beech	*Fagus sylvatica*
Oak	*Quercus robur*
Plane	*Platanus orientalis*

Weeds

Dandelion	*Taraxacum spp*
Mugwort	*Artemesia vulgaris*
Nettle	*Urtica dioica*
Pellitory	*Parietaria officinalis*
Plantain	*Plantago lanceolata*
Ragweed	*Ambrosia artemisiifolia*

Food allergy

The concept that certain foods can produce adverse reactions in susceptible individuals has a long history. Hippocrates (460-370 BC) reported that cows milk could cause gastric upset and urticaria. Later Gallen (210-131 BC) described a case of intolerance to goat's milk, and it was Lucretius (95-51BC) who said "what is food to one man may be poison to others". In 1912 Schloss made noteworthy attempts to study individual cases. Prior to this reports of food intolerance in medical literature were anecdotal (David, 1993).

The subject of food allergy is complex and a large part of the subject is beyond the author's expertise or objectives in writing this book. However the following quote will serve to illustrate current views and opinions. "In view of the complexity of foods and the difficulties encountered in food allergen isolation/characterisation, is the identification and characterisation of these food components that induce allergic reactions necessary, particularly since the only proven treatment for food allergy is avoidance?" (Lehrer, 1997). However as demonstrated by the number of deaths or serious reactions to foods that occur each year, avoidance by a highly sensitive subject is not always possible (Yunginger, 1988). Furthermore, in the future food avoidance may prove to be even more difficult. Many of the new foods which are being developed are based on materials which do not even remotely resemble the original source of the food, such as surimi fish based products that can cause allergic reactions in fish allergic subjects (Musmand, 1992).

Also a number of genetically altered foods that are being produced or considered for production based on DNA technology are being proposed for human consumption (Harlander, 1991; Kessler, 1992), and there is concern about the allergenicity of such new proteins that are being introduced into our diet. Better identification and increased knowledge of major food allergens will lead to improved reagents for diagnosis and treatment of food allergy, and standardisation of food-allergenic extracts. Since these treatments are based on our understanding of allergens, major food allergens must be characterised and their epitopes identified for use in new treatment (O'Hehir, 1993; de Vries & Lamb, 1994). Thus further research into the identification, characterisation and study of food-allergen structure is essential.

Testing is relevant in infants with gastro-intestinal symptoms, in children with atopic dermatitis and chronic asthma, and in a few adults with severe disease particularly with symptoms from more than one organ system, an appropriately obvious case history, a history of life threatening reaction where there is uncertainty about the offending food (Mygind, 1996).

Table 4 The criteria against testing for foods

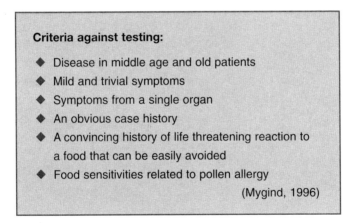

Criteria against testing:

◆ Disease in middle age and old patients

◆ Mild and trivial symptoms

◆ Symptoms from a single organ

◆ An obvious case history

◆ A convincing history of life threatening reaction to a food that can be easily avoided

◆ Food sensitivities related to pollen allergy

(Mygind, 1996)

Common foods causing allergy:

Cow's milk	Cereals/grains, flour
Hen's eggs	Legumes, peanuts, soya bean
Fish/shell fish	Fruit and vegetables
Tree nuts	Seeds, sesame, aniseed, caraway, dill

Latex allergy

Natural rubber is obtained from the rubber tree, Hevea Brasiliensis. The milky sap from this plant, latex, contains a rubber matrix of polyisoprene, about 2% protein and water. During rubber manufacture, the polyisoprene chains are cross-linked and many chemicals are added (vulcanisers, accelerators, stabilisers, antioxidants). The final product contains a number of chemicals (Type IV allergy) and at least 16 protein molecules which are the cause of IgE-mediated Type I reaction (Fuchs, 1992). Latex allergens show cross-reactivity with fruit allergens. The most frequently mentioned are banana, avocado and kiwi.

Latex allergy is increasing, often goes unrecognised and is under-investigated. The increasing incidence is ascribed to new manufacturing methods (Lane & Lee, 1997). Latex is a widespread product and the variety of articles containing latex is considerable. The most important are gloves, medical equipment (catheters, tubes, dental dams), condoms and balloons (Levy, 1994; Turjanmaa, 1987).

Almost anyone can become sensitive to latex. The most vulnerable are people who have an atopic background, people who suffer from hand eczema, patients who undergo multiple operations and patients who are chronically exposed to latex medical devices. Children with Meningomyelocene, Spina Bifida or who have severe urogenital defects are also vulnerable with an incidence ranging from 20-60%.

Latex is an important cause of occupational allergy among health care workers (Lagier, 1992) and with workers in the latex industry. A study of rubber industry workers showed a positive skin test response to latex in 10% of those tested (Levy, 1994). However the prevalence of latex allergy in the general population is not known (Lane & Lee, 1987).

APPENDIX 2: ALLERGY QUESTIONNAIRE

Patient Ref. No._____

Date of Assessment:

N.A.D.A.S.

NORFOLK ALLERGY DIAGNOSTIC AND ADVISORY SERVICE
ALLERGY ASSESSMENT QUESTIONNAIRE

Referring Doctor: _____   Surgery / Hospital: _____

PATIENT'S SURNAME:	FORENAME:	M/F	M/S/D/ P
ADDRESS:	D.O.B.		

SYMPTOMS:

Seasonal Rhinitis		Perennial Rhinitis		Irritation of Eyes or Swelling of Eyelids	
Nonseasonal Asthma		Sneezing		Irritation of Throat and Palate	
Seasonal Asthma		Discharge		Eczema or Skin Irritation, Urticaria	
Ears: Itching		Nose Bleeds		Other Rashes	
Crackling		Rhinorrhea		Diarrhoea, Vomitting, Constipation, Bloated Feeling	
Popping		Sinusitis		Wind or Indigestion, Stomach Pains	
Deafness		Smell/Taste		Migraine or Recurrent Headaches	
		Blocking		Sleep Disturbance	
		Itching			
Additional Info.:-					

Have you ever smoked?   Do you smoke now?   Are you a non-smoking household?

Which symptoms bother you the most? _____

Severity of symptoms: MILD: MODERATE: SEVERE:

Age at Onset:

Any reaction to Insect Stings?   Yes/No   Any reaction to Aspirin?   Yes/No

Any reactions to Latex Rubber?   Yes/No   Any reaction to other drugs? _____

TIMING OF SYMPTOMS: Are the symptoms.   All Year?   and / or   Seasonal?

If Seasonal indicate which Months

Jan	Feb	Mar	Apr	May	Jun	Jul	Aug	Sep	Oct	Nov	Dec

1

TIMING OF SYMPTOMS cont.

Holidays:
When away from home are your symptoms usually: Better.   Worse.   The same.

IF SEASONAL: Immediate / Some hours later / Both

ARE YOU AFFECTED BY:-   **ARE YOU BETTER:-**

Trees		Grasses	
Weeds		Cereals	
Moulds			

	Yes/No
In wet weather during the Summer	
If you go indoors	

IF PERENNIAL :   Constant / Intermittent

ARE YOU AFFECTED BY:-

Wet		Summer	
Dry		Winter	
Hot		Indoors	
Cold		Outdoors	

HAVE YOU NOTICED THAT SYMPTOMS COME ON:

At any special time of the day or night?   Yes / No   If Yes when?   _____

In any particular room of the house?   Yes / No   If Yes which one?   _____

Which of the following can make your symptoms worse?

House Dust		Bed Making		Vacuuming/Dusting		Tobacco Smoke		Changes in Temp	
Emotion		Stress		Odours		Exertion		Infections	

ENVIRONMENT.   Birth Place?   Age of present house?
                        Grew up where?   How long lived in?
Details of House:

In Town	In Village	In Country	Dry	Damp	Any Moulds Present

Type of Bedroom Furnishings

	Yes	No
Feather Pillows/Duvet/Eiderdown		
Feathers elsewhere in the house		
Curtains		
Carpets		
Soft Toys		

Type of Bed:		Type of Mattress:	
Pine		Interior Sprung	
Bunk		Foam	
Divan		Horsehair	
Boxspring		Other	
		Age of Mattress	

Heating in the house

Radiators	
Ducted warm air	
Paraffin or Calor gas	
Open fires	
Cooker type	

Type of Vacuum Cleaner	
Age of Vacuum Cleaner	
Filtration Level	
Number of House Plants	
Any Moulds Present	

2

ANIMALS:

Contact:	Indoors		Outdoors		Day-care		School		Work			
Type:	Cat		Dog		Gerbil		**Hamster**		Caged Birds		Rabbit	
	Horse		Rats		Mice		Cows		Sheep		Poultry	
	Other											

DAY CARE / SCHOOL / WORK ENVIRONMENT

Occupation: _____

Affected at Work / School   Yes / No

How affected? _____
_____

Have you missed school / work as a result of the symptoms?   Yes / No

How many days lost? _____

HOBBIES:
_____

PAST ALLERGIC HISTORY
_____
_____
_____
_____
_____
_____

FOOD / DRINK HISTORY:
_____
_____
_____
_____
_____

FAMILY HISTORY:

	Father	Mother	Paternal Relatives	Maternal Relatives	Brothers / Sisters	Children
Allergies						
Chest Disorders						
Skin Disorders						
Seasonal/Perennial Rhinitis						
Others						

What previous illnesses, hospitalisation or operations have you had?
_____
_____

78

WHAT TYPE OF TREATMENTS HAVE YOU HAD?

		Helpful or not?
Tablets and Type		
Inhalers e.g. Ventolin (Relievers)		
Preventors		
Steroid Tablets e.g. Prednislone		
Steroid Injections		
Skin Treatment e.g. Steroid Creams		

Previous Allergy Investigations

	Yes / No	Where / When	Results if known
Have you ever seen an allergist?			
Have you ever been skin tested?			
Have you ever been hyposensitised?			
Have you ever had a patch or blood test?			

SKIN PRICK TEST:

Time of Test:

CONTROLS:-   **Negative**   **Positive**

Allergens:		

CONCLUSIONS / PLAN OF ACTION:

79

Patient Ref. No. _____

N.A.D.A.A.S.

Date of Assessment:

Nᴏʀꜰᴏʟᴋ Aʟʟᴇʀɢʏ Dɪᴀɢɴᴏꜱᴛɪᴄ Aɴᴅ Aᴅᴠɪꜱᴏʀʏ Sᴇʀᴠɪᴄᴇ

ALLERGY ASSESSMENT QUESTIONNAIRE

Food and Drinks History

Referring Doctor: _____   Surgery / Hospital: _____

PATIENT'S SURNAME: ADDRESS:	FORENAME: D.O.B.	M/F	M/S/D/P

INFANT FEEDING

Birth Weight:- _____ lbs _____ ozs

Breast feeding:-   Yes / No / Not known

Duration of breast feeding:-   1, 2, 3, 4, 5, 6, 7, 8, 9, 10, 11, 12 months

Were supplementary feeds given?   Yes / No   If yes, when were these started ____ weeks

If not breast fed, what milk was given? _____

ANY FEEDING DIFFICULTIES?	
EXCESSIVE VOMITING?	
EXCESSIVE CONSTIPATION, DIARRHOEA OR NAPPY RASH?	
DIFFICULTY IN WEANING?	

Weaned at _____ months.   Any reaction on introduction of new foods? _____

Name of foods: _____

Additional Information / Main reason for referral.

ADULTS

Are you on any special diet? _____   How long for? _____

Does any food cause indigestion? _____

Has any food ever caused a rash? _____

Has any food made your symptoms worse? _____

Does any drink make your symptoms worse? _____

How much food and drink is required to produce symptoms? _____

How long after do symptoms appear? _____ (Hours / Minutes)

Do you brew wine and/or beer at home?   Yes / No

If "yes", for how long? _____

Do you bake your own bread with yeast?   Yes / No

If "yes", does it affect you?   Yes / No

Do you think you may be allergic to any of the following: (please tick)

Shell Fish		Cow's Milk		Tea		Chemicals	
Fish		Goat's Milk		Coffee		Preservatives	
Pork		Cheese		Beer		Dyes	
Peanut		Eggs		Wine		Drugs	
Nut		Yeast		Spirits		Latex/Rubber	
Citrus Fruits		Wheat		Soft Drinks			
Fruits		Other Cereals		Chocolate			
Vegatables							

How do they affect you? (Please tick)

Swelling of lips / tongue		Indigestion		Vomiting		Diarrhoea		Stomach Pains	
Sneezing		Stuffy Nose		Asthma		Skin Rashes		Itch	
Urticaria		Angio-Oedema		Eczema		Migraine		Deafness	
Malaise		Itchy Eyes		Depression		Anxiety		Hyperactivity	
Other									

Additional Information

2

Food and Drinks History Continued

SKIN PRICK TEST :

Time of Test :

CONTROLS :-   **Negative**   **Positive**

Allergens:

CONCLUSIONS / PLAN OF ACTION:

3

APPENDIX 3: ALLERGY PROTOCOL

PracticeNursing

Allergy protocol

The risk of development of asthma in children with allergic rhinitis may be as high as 50 per cent. If existing asthma therapies and avoidance measures are shown to modify long-term morbidity from asthma, then investigation and treatment of patients with rhinitis should be a priority.

The treatment of ongoing chronic asthma and rhinitis involves a thorough evaluation of the patient, their environment and treatment management (Kay, 1992).

The following protocol has been designed as a baseline for GPs and practice nurses developing their own protocols to help identify the patient's condition, institute avoidance measures and prescribe appropriate treatment, with the ultimate objective to improve quality of life and minimal treatment dependence.

It involves seven stages, as detailed below.

Stage 1: Observation

Observe the patient's colour; does the patient demonstrate any of the following:
Periorbital oedema/allergic shiners.
Dennie-Morgan intraorbital folds, common in milk allergy in children.
Allergic nasal crease, (across bridge of nose, caused by patient persistently rubbing nose in upward manner, i.e. allergic salute).
Other mannerisms to relieve nasal itch.
Swollen or congested nose, (shape of nose can suggest polyps).

Stage 2: Listening

Nasal tone: does patient sound blocked?
Can you hear wheezing during normal course of conversation.
Is patient dyspnoeic?

Stage 3: Recording the history

Leading questions are essential, as patients will often withhold information because they fear disbelief. Patients are very capable of making unusual observations, which can prove to be most significant. For perennial and seasonal rhinitis ask whether the patient has any of the following symptoms:
Sneezing.
Nasal discharge, both frontal and post nasal.
Type of discharge, thick, clear or rhinorrhoea.
Nasal blocking; bilateral, alternate sides, only on one side, polyps.
Anosmia.
Irritation/swelling of eyes.
Irritation of throat/mouth/palate.
Headaches, frequency/are they associated with nasal symptoms?
Ears, do they itch, crackle or pop?
Asthma, apply already well established questions.
Sleep disturbance.
Are the symptoms all the year round/intermittent throughout the year/or seasonal?
How soon on going outdoors do the symptoms start?
How soon on contact with known allergens would the symptoms start?
Are the symptoms better/worse/same, away from home or abroad?
How soon on return home would the symptoms start?
Are the symptoms worse at home/school/work or worse at any particular time of the day or night?
Do changes in temperature, fumes/cigarette smoke, dusting/vacuuming/bed making affect symptoms?
What age did symptoms develop?
Length of time lived in your present house/school/work?
Age of house.
Is the house damp/is there a cellar/is there a well in the garden?
How is the house heated?
Describe bedding/curtains/carpet/toys in bedroom.
Are there feather pillows/cushions in bedroom/lounge?
Are there plants in the house?

What pets are there at home/school/work?
What is the patient's occupation?
What are the patient's hobbies?
Drug allergies, sensitivity to additives/syrups/flavourings?
Does the patient smoke/ever smoked?
The age of the patient bears some relevance to the cause of allergy:
Two years - possibly foods causing problems.
Two to 40 years - usually inhalant allergies.
Over 40 years - not many clues available, therefore much questioning required.
Sex of patient - more boys than girls develop allergies.
Family history - look for history of symptoms similar to patient's and possible allergy history in both sides of the family for three generations.
Previous treatment and efficacy.
Special expertise is required in the area of food allergy - referral is recommended.
Hormonal influences.
Is the patient hyperreactive?
Vasomotor - nose not usually itchy.
Emotional.
Drug induced - aspirin sensitivity, medicamentosa.
Sometimes the history does not point to the allergens;
for instance, many mould spores are allergenic but may be difficult to incriminate because they are not common
Mould allergy should be suspected if symptoms are worse in the late summer and autumn.

Stage 4: Skin tests

Demonstrating positive skin tests are useful in order to:
Establish the existence of atopy.
Persuade patients to take measures to contain house allergen exposure or to part with pets.
House dust mites are associated with the two types of diseases discussed. No mite/allergen eradication measures should be done without appropriate medical supervision, advice and proper diagnosis of allergy to domestic allergens. Anti-allergen product manufacturers should convey this message clearly on all products and advertising.
(Colloff *et al*, 1992).

Stage 5: Avoidance

The avoidance procedure is dependent upon the allergens identified. Bedding protection covers are effective. Substances that kill mites via chemical action, termed acaricides, range from caffeine to highly potent (and toxic to humans) organophosphates. The application of the substances in the home has raised a a number of, as yet, unanswered questions. Chronic exposure and proximity of exposure, given the site to which acaricides are applied, will raise further questions on safety. Overall application of acaricides to fabrics with which children are likely to have prolonged close contact, e g. mattresses and pillows, is not recommended.

Stage 6: Treatments

Treatments for asthma have been clearly documented elsewhere. The mainstay for rhinitis are antihistamines, cromoglycates, anticholinergic sprays and topical corticosteroids. For long-term intranasal steroid maintenance treatment, drops should be avoided to prevent significant systemic absorption: the sprays should be used instead.
Seasonal asthma and rhinitis treatment should commence two to four weeks prior to their known season. In addition time should be spent on advising the patient about the correct way to instil drops and apply nasal sprays. They should be warned about some over the counter products causing rhinitis medicamentosa.

Stage 7: Evaluation

Periods of evaluation of patient's progress with regard to asthma care are well documented. The periods are ideal opportunities to evaluate the benefits and progress for the rhinitis patient. This is easily achievable when patients are multi-symptomatic, i.e. asthma and rhinitis.

Notes

Protected time should be afforded to the patient with rhinitis and other associated symptoms without asthma, in order to prevent the development of asthma and afford early recognition and institute appropriate treatment as necessary.

The protocol outlined here requires the maximum time and skills in order to offer the best help and benefit to the patient.
It is therefore suggested that each professional tailors the protocol according to his/her time and professional limitations.

It should be remembered that symptoms from allergic rhinitis may be indistinguishable from vasomotor rhinitis and that the two may co-exist.

References
Colloff M J et al (1992)
    The control of allergens to dust mite and
    domestic pets; a position paper', *Clinical and
    Experimental Allergy* **22**: Supp 2, 1-28.
Kay A B Lessoff M (1992)
    'Allergic to house dust mite, allergy conventional
    and alternative concepts'. A report from the
    Royal College of Physicians committee on clinical
    immunology and allergy, *Clinical and
    Experimental Allergy* **22**: Supp 1

Written by
Mary Brydon
Allergy Nurse Practitioner

Appendix 4: Glossary

Allergen: A foreign protein or hapten which induces the
                              formation of anaphylactic antibodies and which may
                              precipitate an allergic response.

Allergenic: Behaving like an allergen.

Allergy: a) Initially embraced immunology; but now focused
                              on the host tissue – damaging or irritation effects of
                              immunological responses. (Holgate & Church 1993).
                              b) When a substance, which is not harmful in itself,
                              causes an immune response and a reaction that
                              gives rise to symptoms and diseases in a few
                              predisposed individuals only (Mygind, 1996).

Anaphylactoid reaction: An allergic-like reaction but produced by
                              non-immunological mechanisms.

Anaphylaxis: a) The consequences of an allergic reaction in an
                              isolated organ or systemically.
                              b) Frequently mediated through IgE antibodies, the
                              generalised reactions involve respiratory,
                              cardio-vascular and gastro-intestinal systems, and
                              skin, singly or in combinations. Death is due to
                              suffocation (laryngeal oedema and asthma) or
                              cardiac arrest (hypotension and arrhythmia).

Antibody: A molecule produced by the immune system in
                              response to an antigen which has the property of
                              combining specifically with the antigen which
                              induced its formation.

Antigen: A molecule which induces the formation of antibody.

Anti serum: Serum containing antibodies to a specific antigen.

Arthus: a) Type III reaction. Antigen-antibody complex, onset in four to six hours after exposure, maximal in six hours, fades over next few hours. Examples, industrial inhalants, farmer's lung, allergic aspergillosis.
                   b) Experimental localised acute necroting vasculitis, first described as local anaphylaxis.

Atopy: The ability to produce IgE antibodies to common allergens; demonstrable by RAST or skin prick test.

Axon reflex: Local propagation of a nerve reflex by retrograde or antidromic stimulation of nerve axons resulting in the release of neuropeptides.

Challenge: Administration of an implicated allergen to an allergic subject, in order to provoke an allergic response.

Dermatographism: Also known as dermographia and factitious urticaria, is a condition in which tracings made on the skin leave a distinct swollen reddish mark. The stimulus of scratching the skin produces an excessive amount of histamine.

Desensitisation: A protocol of repeated injections of allergen or modified allergen with the aim of reducing a patient's allergic responsiveness to that allergen.

Electrophoresis: The migration of charged particles between electrodes. If a spot or streak of solution containing a protein is applied to filter paper, which has been soaked in a buffer solution, then after some time an electrical potential difference will appear between the ends.

Epitope: A single antigenic determinant. Functionally it is the portion of an antigen which combines with the antibody paratope.

Fc_ε R1: Receptors in mast cell membrane capable of binding with high affinity portion of IgE. Cross linkage of two or more IgE molecules to bring their receptors into juxtaposition, initiates a sequence of biochemical events which results in degranulation to release histamine, proteases and heparin.

Hapten: A small molecule which is incapable of inducing an antibody response by itself but can, when bound to a protein carrier, act as an epitope, e.g. penicilloic acid.

Histamine: A major vasoactive amine released from mast cells and basophil granules. It is a preformed mediator, which is of considerable importance in conjunctivitis, rhinitis and urticaria.

Hyper-reactivity: A state of increased reactivity to a provoking stimulus e.g. Bronchial hyper-reactivity in asthma. Specifically a greater magnitude of response to a given concentration of stimulus.

Hypersensitivity: Synonymous with allergy.

IgE: One of the five different types of immunoglobulin (antibodies) in man. IgE possesses reagin activity and is the anaphylactic antibody in man. It is of paramount importance for atopic allergy.

Immunoglobulins: Described as the smallest tool in the world (Mygind, 1996). Human immunoglobulins (antibodies) belong to five classes, IgG, IgA, IgM, IgD and IgE.

Kallidins:	Either one or two types of polypeptides released by blood plasma globulin one of which is Bradykinin.
Kallikrein:	An enzyme that breaks down proteins in blood plasma, pancreatic juice, and other body fluids there by releasing Kallidins.
Ligand:	A linking or binding molecule, usually used to define a specific antigenic determinant to which an antibody binds.
Mast cell:	Is the primary initiating cell of IgE mediated allergic reactions. There are two types i.e. connective tissue mast cells (MC_{TC}) and mucosal mast cells (MC_T). They also release tryptase and chymase. Mast cells are important for the expression of symptoms in allergic rhinitis and urticaria. Their role for asthma and atopic dermatitis seem far less significant.
Mediators:	A chemical substance released by one cell which stimulates another, e.g. mast cell mediators.
Oedema:	Tissue swelling due to extravasation of plasma proteins.
Paratope:	The part of an antibody molecule which makes contact with the antigenic determinant (Epitope).
Pathogen:	An organism which causes disease.
Primary response:	The immune response (cellular or humoral) following an initial encounter with a particular antigen, synonymous with sensitisation.
RAST: (Radioallergosorbent Test)	A laboratory technique for the detection of circulating IgE with specific allergen determinants.

Reagin: One of a group of antibodies that reacts with the
                          allergens.

Receptor: A specific protein or group of proteins usually on the
                          cell surface, capable of recognising and binding a
                          specific ligand.

Saprophytic;   Any vegetable organism that lives on decaying
                          organic matter e.g. mushrooms, moulds, mildew,
                          bacteria.

Secondary response: The immune response which follows a second or
                          subsequent encounter with a particular antigen.

Sensitisation: The stimulation of allergic antibody production
                          usually by an initial encounter to a specific allergenic
                          substance. Synonymous with primary response.

Skin Prick Test: The detection of an IgE response to a specific
                          allergen through the induction of a weal-and-flare
                          response by pricking the skin through droplets of the
                          allergen.

Tolerance: A state of specific immunological unresponsiveness.

Weal: An area of oedema produced at the site of
                          intradermal introduction of an allergen, histamine or
                          similar provocant. Stimulation of axon reflexes in the
                          weal area gives rise to the larger flare response.

APPENDIX 5: REFERENCES AND FURTHER READING

References

Basomba A. EAACI '93. Subcommittee on Skin Tests. Evaluation of Changes in Skin Sensitivity by Means of Skin Tests. Allergy 1993;14:71-75.

Berrens L. et al. Enzimatic Properties of Cat Allergen 1 (*Fel d* I) J. Clinical & Experimental Allergy 1990; 20(1):6.

Björkstén F. et al Assay of the Biologic Activity of Allergen Skin Test Preparations. J. Allergy and Clinical Immunology 1984;73: 324-351.

Bousquet J. Pathophysiology of Skin Tests. EAACI Subcommittee on Skin Tests. Allergy 1993;14:50-54.

Burrows B. et al Respiratory Disorders and Allergy Skin Test Reactions. Annals of Internal Medicine 1976; 84:134-139.

Charpin C. et al *Fel d* I Allergen Distribution in Cat Fur and Skin. Allergy and Clinical Immunology News (1991A);1:408.

Chinn S. et al Measuring Atopy in a Multi-centre Epidemiology Study. European J. Epidemiology 1996;12:155-162.

Colloff M. J. et al The Control of Dust Mites and Domestic Pets. A Position paper. J. Clinical & Experimental Allergy 1992;22:1-28.

Coombs R.R.A.&   The Classification of Allergic Reactions Responsible
Gell P.G.H.   for Clinical Hypersensitivity and Disease   1975.
                        Clinical Aspects of Immunology, 3rd. Edition;
                        p 761-781.
                        Blackwell Scientific Publications.

Cromia F. E.   Experimental Histamine Pruritis 1. Influence of
                        Physician and Psychological Factors on Threshold
                        Reactivity.
                        Journal Invest. Dermatology 1952;19:21-24.

Daniel A.   Comments and Proceedings of the Task Force on
                        Guidelines for Standardisation Old & New
                        Technologies used for the Diagnosis and Treatment
                        of Allergic Disorders.
                        J. Allergy & Clinical Immunology 1990;85:138-139.

David T. J.   Food and Food Additive Intolerance in Childhood.
                        1993. Blackwell Scientific Publications.
                        ISBN 0-632-03487-4.

De Groot H. et al   Affinity Purification of a Major and a Minor Allergen
                        from Dog Extract: Serological Activity of
                        Affinity-Purified *Can f* I and of *Can f* I-depleted
                        Extract.
                        J. Allergy & Clinical Immunology 1991;87(6):
                        1056-1065.

De Vries J. E.   Immunotherapy with Allergen Derived Epitopes.
& Lamb J. R.   Allergy & Clinical Immunology, News, 1994;6:49-53.

Dolovich J. et al   Late Cutaneous Allergic Responses in isolated IgE
                        dependent reactions.
                        J. Allergy & Clinical Immunology 1973;52:38-46.

Dreborg S.   Folia Allergology, Immunology. Clinica 1988;35:3-11.
                              Pub. Lombardo Editore, Via Verona 22 00161
                              Roma.

Dreborg S.   Skin Tests Used in Type I Allergy Testing.
                              Position Paper EAACI Subcommittee
                              Allergy Supplement10; Vol 44.
                              Munksgaard, Copenhagen 1989.

Dreborg S.   Allergy to Apple, Carrot and Potato in Children with
& Fouchard T.   birch pollen allergy. Allergy 1983:38;167-171.

Dreborg S. & Frew A.   Position Papers: Allergen Standardisation and Skin
                              Tests. EAACI '93 Subcommittee on Skin Tests.
                              Allergy 1993; Supplement No. 14: 48-82.

Egmar et al   Direct and Indirect Exposure to Cat (*Fel d* I) and
                              Dog (*Can f* I) Allergens in the Home.
                              J. Allergy & Clinical Immunology 1993;91(1):733.

Evans III R.   Clinical Aspects of Hymonoptera Hypersensitivity.
& Summers R. J.   Monograph on Insect Allergy. 1986. AAAAI
                              Committee on Insects. Ed; Levine & Lockey.
                              Second Edition.

Ewan P. W.   Clinical Study of Peanut and Nut Allergy in 62
                              Consecutive Patients: New Features and
                              Associations. BMJ 1990 (April);312:1074-1078

Fireman P.   Atlas of Allergies 1991.
& Slavin R.G.   Gower Medical Publications, London
                              ISBN 0-397-44669-1

Fjeldsgaard B. E. et al   Comparison of IgE - Binding Antigens in Horse
                              Dander and a Mixture of Horse Hair & Skin
                              Scrapings. Allergy 1993;48:535-541.

Frankland W.

Confirming the History by the use of Skin Tests.
Mims Magazine. February 1985:17.

Frew A. J.

Skin Tests.
Chapter 61, Allergy & Allergic Diseases 1997;
1007-1011. Edited by B Kay, Blackwell Science
Ltd. Oxford. ISBN 0-86542-867-0.

Frew A. J.

Skin tests in Clinical Practice & Epidemiology.
J. Clinical & Experimental Allergy 1992;2:881-882

Fuchs T. et al

Immediate Reactions to Rubber Products.
Allergy Proceedings 1992;13:61-66.

Gallant & Maibach

Reproducibility of allergy epicutaneous techniques.
J. Allergy & Clinical Immunology 1973;51:252-262.

Gaughan M. A. et al

Skin prick testing is a safe method of confirming
food hypersensitivity. Poster display, Allergy
Diagnosis
June 25 1998 Allergy Supplement No. 43;53:191.

Glinert R. et al

Fel d I is markedly reduced following sequential
washing of cats. AAAA&I Proceedings 1990.

Gottlieb S.

Antihistamine drug withdrawn by manufacturer.
BMJ. July 1999;319:7.

Grundbacher F.

Causes of Variation in Serum IgE Levels in Normal
Populations.
J. Allergy & Clinical Immunology 1975;56:104-111.

Haahtela T.

Skin tests in epidemiologic studies.
EAACI Sub-committee on skin tests.
Allergy 1993; Supplement 14: 76-80.

Halliwell R. E. W. et al   The RAST Test in the diagnosis of canine atopy
                            disease.
                            J. Allergy & Clinical Immunology 1978;62(4):
                            236-242

Harlander S. K.   Biotechnology - A Means of Improving our Food
                            Supply.
                            Food Technology 1991;45:841,886,891-92 & 895.

Hattevig G. et al   Clinical Symptoms and IgE responses to common
                            food proteins and inhalants in the first seven years
                            of life. Clinical Allergy 1987;17:571-578.

Hide D.   Skin & patch testing in diagnosis of allergic disease.
                            Proceedings BSACI Allergy School,
                            Appleton Tower Sept. 1989.

Holgate S. T.   Allergy. Gower Medical Publishing.
& Church M.   London 1993: 1.3, 11.5, 11.6. ISBN 0-397-44725-6

Holgerson M. et al   The Precision of Skin Test with Phazet TNM, The
                            Østerballe needle & the Bifurcated Needle.
                            Allergy 1985;40(4):64-65.

Horak F.   Manifestation of allergic rhinitis in latent sensitised
                            patients.
                            A Prospective Study.
                            Arch. Otorhinolaryngol. 1985; 242:224-239.

Hourihane J. O'B. et al   Peanut Allergy in relation to heredity, maternal diet,
                            and other atopic diseases: BMJ. 1996(8);
                            313:518-521.

Jackson W. F. et al   A Colour Atlas of Allergy.
                            Wolfe Medical publications 1988.
                            ISBN 0723409145.

Jarvis D. & Burney P.   The Epidemiology of Allergic Disease.
BMJ 1998(2);316:607-610.

Jarvis D. & Burney P.   Epidemiology of Atopy and Atopic Disease.
Allergy and allergic diseases. Edited A.B. Kay,
Chapter 77:1208-1224. Blackwell Scientific
Publications 1997 Oxford. ISBN 0-86542-867-0.

Juhlin-Dannfeldt C.   About the occurrence of various forms of pollen
allergy in Sweden.
ACTA Med Scand 1948;26:563-577.

Kalogeromitros D. et al   Influence of the menstrual cycle on skin prick test
reactions to histamine, morphine and allergen.
J. Clinical & Experimental Allergy 1995;25:461-466

Kalveram C. M. et al   House Dust Mite in Cat Epithelia - A common
allergen.
J. Allergy & Clinical Immunology
1993;48(16):2243.

Kessler O. A. et al   The safety of foods developed by Biotechnology.
Science 1992;256:1747-1832.

Knysak D. J.   Animal Aeroallergens.
Immunology & Allergy Clin N.A. August 1989.

Lagier F. et al   Prevalence of Latex Allergy in Operating Room
Nurses.
J. Allergy & Clinical Immunology. 1992:90;319-322.

Lane S. J. & Lee T. H.   Anaphylaxis.
Allergy & Allergic Disease. 1997;l2(100):1550-1572.
Edited by AB Kay. Blackwell Science.
ISBN 0-86542-867-0.

Lehrer S. et al

Food Allergens.
Allergy & Allergic Diseases 1997;2(58):
Edited by A B Kay. Blackwell Science.
ISBN 0-86542-867-0.

Levy D. A. et al

Allergy to Latex.
Allergy 1994;47:579-587.

Lewis T. et al

Vascular reactions of the skin to injury. Part II. The
liberation of a histamine-like substance in injured
skin. The underlying cause of factitious urticaria and
of wheals produced by burning and observation
upon nervous control of certain skin diseases.
Heart II, 1927: 209-218.

Lindgren S. et al

Breed-specific dog-danduff allergens.
J. Allergy & Clinical Immunology 1988;82:196.

Luczynska C. et al

Aerodynamic size and levels of airborne cat
allergen (*Fel d* I) and its relevance to asthma.
Allergy Proceedings.1988;II(6):138 (abstract).

Malling H. J.

General Aspects of skin prick testing.
EAACI Sub-committee on Skin Tests.
Allergy 1993; Supp 14:48-82.

Malling H. J.

Reproducibility of skin sensitivity using a
quantitative skin prick test.
Allergy 1985; 40:400-404.

Meding B. et al

Late skin prick test reactions to malted wheat.
Clinical observations & immunohistochemical
characterisation.
Allergy. 1998(3);53(3):282-288.

Muscato G.

Allergy to horse danders in occupationally exposed subjects.
Annuals of Allergy 1990. Abstract 31 Presented at 47th Annual Meeting of American College of Allergy & Immunology.
No 10-14. San Francisco. Calfornia.

Musmand J. J. et al

Surimi: A hidden, potentially serious cause of fish allergy. American Allergy 1992;70:53.

Mygind N. et al

Essential Allergy, 2nd Edition.
Blackwell Science. Oxford. 1996.
ISBN 0-632-03645-1.

Nolan D.

Food Allergy / Allergy in Practice.
Update 1999; 7th May:875-882.

Novembre E. et al

Case Report - Skin-prick-test induced anaphylaxis.
Allergy 1995;50:511-513.

O'Hehir R. et al

T Cell Epitopes, MCH Antigens and their Application in Molecular Biology and Immunology of Allergens.
1993:63-68. Editors D.K. Kraft and A. Sehon.
CRC Press, Boca Raton.

Ollier S. & Davies R.

Skin Prick test preparations of Dermatophagoids pteronyssinus for prediction of a positive response to provocation testing.
J. Clinical & Experimental Allergy 1989;19:457-462.

Orren A. & Dowdle E.

The Effects of Age and Sex on Serum IgE Concentrations in Three Ethnic Groups.
Int. Arch. Appl. Immunology. 1975;48:824-835.

Pasterello A.E.

Skin tests for the diagnosis of IgE-Mediated Allergy
Allergy 1993;48:57-62.

Peat J. K.
& Woodcock A. J.

Sensitivity to Common Allergens: Relation to
Respiratory Symptoms and Bronchial
Hyper-responsiveness in children from three
different climate areas of Australia.
J. Clinical & Experimental Allergy 1991;21:573-581.

Pepys J.

Skin Testing.
British Journal of Hospital Medicine,
Oct.1975:413-417.

Perez-Santos C.

Allergy to Animals.
1995. Iatros Edicions. S.L. Barcelona.
ISBN: 847714-099-5.

Ring J. et al

High Incidence of Horse serum protein allergy in
various autoimmune disorders.
J. Allergy & Clinical Immunology.1997;59(3):
185-189.

Sampsom H. et al

Food Allergy – Adverse Reactions to Foods and
Food Additives. 1991; 7: 99-112. Blackwell Scientific
Publications, Inc. Boston, USA.
ISBN 0-86542-094-7.

Scadding G. K.

Medical management of Serous Otitis Media.
Abstract of the 1992 BSACI Annual Conference.
J. Clinical & Experimental Allergy. 1993(2);23;
Supp. 1

Schloss O. M.

A case of allergy to common foods.
Am, J. Dis. Child, 1912;3:341-362.

Schou C. et al

Purification and characterisation of the important
dog allergen *Can f* I (Ag 13).
J. Allergy & Clinical Immunology 1990; 85(1):105.

Smith T.F.   Allergy Testing in Clinical Practice.
                           Annals of Allergy 1992(4);68;293-302.

Taudorf E. et al   Reproducibility of skin prick test.
                           Allergy 1985;40:344-349.

Taylor B. et al   Transient IgA. Deficiency and pathogenesus of
                           infantile atopy.
                           Lancet 1973;2:111-115.

Turjanmaa K.   Incidence of immediate allergy to latex gloves in
                           hospital personnel.
                           Contact Dermatology 1987;17:27-35.

Van Asperen P. P. et al Skin test reactivity and clinical allergen sensitivity in
                           infancy.
                           J. Allergy & Clinical Immunology 1984;73:381.

Wood et al   The distribution of cat and dust mite allergen on
                           wall surfaces.
                           J. Allergy & Clinical Immunology 1992;89(i):126-130
                           & 675.

Yunginger J. W. et al   Fatal food induced anaphalaxis
                           JAMA 1988;260:1450-1452.

General publications   European Allergy White Paper. May 1997.
                           ISBN 2-87301-018-5.

                           Vital and Health Statistics. (1986).
                           Percutaneous Immediate Hypersensitivity to Eight
                           Allergens.
                           Data from National Health Survey, Series 11,
                           No. 235, DHSS Publications, No (PHS) 86-1685.

Further reading

Bowman K. L. Pertinent Factors Influencing Comparative Skin Tests on the Arm. J. Allergy 1935;7:39-43.

Clarke C.W. et al Reproducibility of Skin Prick Tests to Five Common Allergens. Clinical Allergy 1982;12:21-25.

Corrigaan E. et al Allergy - Current Medical Literature. 1993 Royal Society of Medicine, ISSN 0968-5625, p5.

Durham S. Tests and Measurement in Asthma & Allergic Rhinitis. Clinical Applications of Immunological Methods. Proceedings BSACI Allergy School, p 10-13 Edinburgh Sept. 1989.

Estelle F. & Simons R. Ancestors of Allergy 1994. Global Medical Communications Ltd. New York. ISBN 0-9639388-6-X.

Haahtela T. & Jokela H. Influence of the Pollen Season on Immediate Skin Test Reactivity to Common Allergens. Allergy 1980;35:15-21.

Illi S. et al Reproducibility of skin prick test results in epidimiologic studies: A Comparison of Two Devices. Allergy 1998;53:353-358.

Lessof M. H. et al Assessing the value of skin prick tests. Clinical Allergy 1980;10:155-120.

Pipkorn U. Pharmacological Influence of Anti-allergic Mediators on in vivo allergen testing. Allergy 1988;43:81-86.

Pipkorn U. et al Topical Dermal Anaesthesia. Assay of biological activity of allergen skin test preparations. Clinical Allergy 1987;17:307-311.

APPENDIX 6

Useful addresses

Anaphylaxis Campaign

PO Box 149
Fleet
Hampshire GU13 9XU

BAF

British Allergy Foundation
Deepdene House
30 Bellgrove Road
Welling
Kent DA16 3PY

BSACI

British Society for Allergy and
Clinical Immunology
BSACI Secretariat
66 Weston Park
Thames Ditton
Surrey KY7 0HL

National Asthma Campaign

Providence House
Providence Place
London N1 0NT

National Eczema Society

163 Eversholt Street
London NW1 1BU

Pollen Research Unit

Worcester College of Higher Education
Henwick Grove
Worcester WR2 6AT

INDEX

CONSOLATION TO US ALL

*"Whenever I have found out that I have blundered
or that my work has been imperfect and when I have been
contemptuously criticised it has been my greatest comfort to say
hundreds of times to myself that I have worked as hard and
as well as I could and no man can do more than this."*

Charles Darwin

Peter Conway lives in Somerset. He is a prolific writer and his novels include *Unwillingly To School, Locked In* and *Deadly Obsession.*

VENGEANCE DEFERRED

Kate Farrant is chairperson of The Frampton Trust, a medical charity. During the night in the basement flat of her gambling club, Kate is overcome by a severe gastro-intestinal disorder and rings for an ambulance. When she later dies in hospital, it's discovered that she has been poisoned. Several people have reason to fear and hate her, and the investigation leads from the gambling club and those who'd worked at The Frampton Trust to the school where she and her psychopathic brother were pupils ten years earlier . . . Only then can any light be shed upon the identity of the murderer . . .

Books by Peter Conway
Published by The House of Ulverscroft:

MURDER IN DUPLICATE
VICTIMS OF CIRCUMSTANCE
CRADLE SNATCH
ONE FOR THE ROAD
CRYPTIC CLUE
LOCKED IN
UNWILLINGLY TO SCHOOL
DESERVING DEATH
DEADLY OBSESSION

PETER CONWAY

VENGEANCE
DEFERRED

Complete and Unabridged

ULVERSCROFT
Leicester

First published in Great Britain in 2009 by
Robert Hale Limited
London

First Large Print Edition
published 2010
by arrangement with
Robert Hale Limited
London

British Library CIP Data

Conway, Peter, *1929 –*
    Vengeance deferred.
    1. Poisoning- -Fiction.
    2. Detective and mystery stories.
    3. Large type books.
    I. Title
    823.9′14–dc22

    ISBN 978–1–84782–971–9

Published by
F. A. Thorpe (Publishing)
Anstey, Leicestershire

Set by Words & Graphics Ltd.
Anstey, Leicestershire
Printed and bound in Great Britain by
T. J. International Ltd., Padstow, Cornwall

This book is printed on acid-free paper

1

Kate Farrant prided herself on never being ill and indeed she hadn't taken a single day's sick leave since she had left school ten years earlier. Tonight, though, was different. It had started in the small hours, when she woke feeling nauseous, and soon after the vomiting began. As she staggered to her feet from her kneeling position bent over the lavatory bowl, she felt the sweat running down her forehead and armpits as she managed to reach the basin. For a few moments she felt a little better after running a damp flannel over her face. The respite only lasted a minute or two and then she bent double, clutched her stomach as the griping pains overcame her, and only just made it back to the lavatory.

She lost track of time, her whole being taken up by the recurring and humiliating episodes, only partly relieved by the drinks of grapefruit juice, diluted with mineral water, which she gulped, trying to assuage the raw feeling in her throat. After one particularly painful episode, though, she had the appalling insight that unless she did something, she was going to die. One thing, though, she was not going to do was to let either Mrs Grant or Jill Corsie see her in this dreadful state, so she somehow crawled across to the table at the side of the bed and just reached her telephone. It required every ounce of her concentration to dial 999 and give the ambulance service the address and tell them that she was alone in the basement flat, before she passed out.

★ ★ ★

Jill Corsie woke suddenly to the thunderous hammering coming from the back garden and at the same time saw the flashing blue light coming from the street outside. She jumped out of bed, hurried into her living room, undid the lock and threw open the sash window on the garden side.

'Hello!' she shouted as loudly as she could. 'What is it?'

The hammering stopped and into the security light behind the building came the figure of an ambulance man.

'Lady dialled 999 from the basement flat at this address, but the door's locked.'

'Hold on, there's another entrance to the flat from inside and I'll be able to let you in through that. I'll come down in just a moment and open the front door of the building for you.'

She hurried out into the corridor and hammered on the door of the adjacent flat. 'Mrs Grant!' she bellowed.

There was a long pause then she heard the sound of footsteps.

'Yes, who is it?'

'An ambulance has arrived to collect Miss Farrant, who's been taken ill. I need you to come down and open the door from the lobby. Please hurry.'

The woman came out soon after, still pulling on her dressing gown. 'What's wrong with her?'

'I don't know, but she's obviously too ill to let them in herself.'

As they hurried down the stairs, not for the first time Jill Corsie cursed the fact that Mrs Grant was the only person in residence whom Kate Farrant trusted with the numbers required to operate the combination lock. She tried to see what digits the woman was putting in, but short of craning her head over her shoulder, there was no way she could do it. And she knew perfectly well that if, in due course, Miss Farrant discovered that she had tried to find out the combination, there would be hell to pay.

'Best you wait up here, miss,' one of the

crew said. 'We shouldn't be long.'

Opening the door and gaining access to the basement flat was the easy part. Getting the stretcher up was another matter altogether, the staircase being both steep and narrow. It seemed an age to Jill, but some ten minutes later, the ambulance men came back up the stairs, with the ashen-faced Kate Farrant, eyes closed, strapped to the stretcher.

'Do you know her?' one of them asked.

'Yes, I work for her. She's the owner of this club.'

The man nodded. 'We're going to take her to St Gregory's Hospital. Why not give them a ring later this morning and the nurse will tell you what to bring. I'm afraid there's a terrible mess down in that flat.'

'All right, thank you. We'll deal with it somehow.'

★ ★ ★

Chief Superintendent Tyrrell had only been in his office at Scotland Yard for a few minutes and was sipping a cappuccino from the dispenser in the rest room along the corridor when his phone rang.

'Tyrrell!'

'It's Brandon here. One of the mandarins at the Home Office has just been on to me.

Evidently a young woman who owns a club called the Spinning Wheel, to which he belongs, has just died under unusual circumstances. She is also the chairperson of a charity of which he is on the board. For obvious reasons he doesn't wish to get involved directly and although he doesn't appear to have any specific worries about the woman's death, he told me that she has been involved in rather too many unusual events in the last year or two for him to accept that her death is just bad luck, particularly as the hospital doesn't appear to have made a specific diagnosis. I know that personally you are tied up at present, but I'd be grateful if you'd get someone on your team to look into it. Your friend Tredgold also did the post mortem and you've always got on well with him, which is more than can be said for the rest of us.'

'Very well, sir.'

As Brandon had said, Roger Tyrrell was busy for the whole of the following week, having to attend a series of meetings on fast-track promotion for those belonging to ethnic minorities in the metropolitan police, and knew that there was no chance of being able to get out of it. Not only was he due to present a discussion paper on the subject, but the commissioner, who was going to be in the

5

chair, had made it quite clear that his presence was mandatory. If there was one thing Tyrrell regretted about his present position it was that it ruled out being able to work on the ground and he missed that greatly. As for his two assistants, Sarah Prescott and Mark Sinclair, he had every confidence in them, both of them being able and conscientious, but he also feared for their promotion prospects. Just because they were well spoken and Mark Sinclair had an Oxford University degree, they looked like becoming victims of the same 'glass ceiling' that the feminists still liked to talk about with reference to their gender. It was ironic, Tyrrell thought, that he should be so involved with the current view that privilege should be done away with in the police force when his own background was so similar to that of Mark Sinclair.

There was no time like the present, Tyrrell thought, and asked his secretary to get the pathologist on the telephone.

There were no introductory remarks or preliminary exchange of niceties from the man when he got through, but Tyrrell had no need of them, recognizing at once the rasping tones of Eric Tredgold, the forensic pathologist.

'Good morning, Eric, some time since I've

spoken to you. Hope you are keeping well.'

'I'm not in a respite home, if that's what you've been thinking, or even hoping. What are you after now?'

'It's something confidential and I can't tell you any details, but suffice it to say that it is concerned with an autopsy you've done on a woman who was admitted to St Gregory's a week ago and died three days later.'

'Ha! I thought that might raise a few anxious looks and raised eyebrows. As it happens, I was about to call you about this very case anyway. Can't tell you any details over the phone; no conversation's safe these days, not even to one in your exalted position. Fix an early time with Miss Graves, would you? And before you ask, she's still alive, even if her appearance at times causes one to wonder.'

'If I am to attend, it'll have to be before the weekend; I'm tied up for the whole of next week.'

'I couldn't possibly do without you entirely, now could I, but under the circumstances you'd better bring those two sidekicks of yours along with you — the plump, cuddly one and that fellow Sinclair. Still making doe eyes at one another, are they, or have they at last got beyond that stage?'

'No comment is the traditional answer to

questions like that and it serves as well as any other. I look forward to seeing you again very soon.'

'You know what, Tyrrell, I've always thought that you'd make a good politician, but it grieves me to discover that you've already become one.'

As Roger Tyrrell had told Tredgold, he was busy for the whole of the following week and there was no chance of his being able to get out of having to attend the meeting.

'I've no idea what exactly Brandon and Tredgold have up their respective sleeves,' he said to his two assistants a little later that morning, 'but the death of this young woman has clearly provoked anxiety amongst the great and good and my guess is that it's something unusual, important or both and I'd like the two of you to come with me to see him. I've arranged an appointment for 8.30 tomorrow morning and we'll take it from there. All right?'

★　★　★

'Miss Graves not here?' Tyrrell asked when they arrived at the pathologist's office at the appointed time.

'Bloody woman's gone to the dentist — can't think why she couldn't wait until I

8

take my holiday in a couple of months' time,' said Tredgold.

'Perhaps the poor soul's in pain,' Tyrrell said.

'If you ask me, a soul was left out of her make-up. People can't put up with anything these days. Stub their big toe on the pavement because they can't be bothered to look where they are going and the first stop's the doctor and the second's a phone call to one of those no-win no-fee sharks. Enough of this nonsense, let us get down to the serious business.

'Four days ago, I carried out an autopsy on a woman, one Ms Kate Farrant, in her late twenties, who's something of a celebrity in her particular circles. I hope you admire my use of the vernacular 'ms', my dear,' he said, grinning at Sarah, 'but in this case, it is not specific enough. She was a miss, unmarried and indeed a virgo intacta, not a very common finding these days in a woman of her age, which appears to have been late twenties, unless they have Sapphic tendencies. I see you look puzzled, my dear,' he said, peering at Sarah over the top of his glasses, which were perched on the tip of his nose. 'Perhaps you might be able to enlighten her, my dear Sinclair. You are usually the fount of all knowledge.'

Sinclair inclined his head slightly. 'Sappho was a sixth-century Greek poetess from Lesbos, who was considered to have had a predilection for those of her own gender, hence its use in educated and literary circles to denote female homosexual inclinations.'

'Capital, my dear fellow. As usual, you don't disappoint me — such admirable and apposite use of the correct syntax. My dear, you still look puzzled.'

'Not puzzled, sir. I was just wondering why you made that assumption.'

'Ah, but I didn't assume anything. If you had been listening attentively, you might remember that I just said that 'it was not a very common finding, unless . . . ''

'Eric,' said Tyrrell firmly, 'reluctant though I am to interrupt this interesting and erudite discussion, I fear that I haven't got all morning.'

'Touché. Let us to business get! The woman, who apart from being the owner of an up-market gambling club in South Kensington, was also the chairperson of a charity called The Frampton Trust, which provides funds for the succour of people with Alzheimer's disease and other forms of dementia. She was in her flat in the basement of this club when she appears to have been stricken with a severe gastro-intestinal disorder in the small hours of Monday last. It

10

is not clear just how long she waited before dialling 999, but by the evidence of the ambulance people it must have been a considerable time because the floors of the bathroom and bedroom were in a terrible state. By the time they got there, she was unconscious and they took her to St Gregory's Hospital where, despite their best endeavours, she died three days later.

'Although they were unable to find a cause for her severe gastroenteritis, their notes about her initial condition and what followed were both detailed and clear. After they had rehydrated her, the woman recovered consciousness, albeit being confused, and she complained bitterly of pins and needles in the extremities, the skin being so sensitive to touch that she had to be nursed under cradles. Her muscles were also exquisitely tender, her tendon reflexes were lost and she finally had a series of convulsions, slipped into a coma and died three days after her admission there. The findings at autopsy were non-specific, but the clinical history strongly suggested to me that the woman had been poisoned and screening tests of blood and urine revealed that the toxic agent was thallium, which fitted the clinical picture.'

Tyrrell nodded. 'I remember the case of Graham Young, who died in Parkhurst prison, it must be a good fifteen years ago. Didn't he poison a number of people with it and kill at least one, eventually dying himself of a heart attack?'

Tredgold raised his eyebrows. 'Your recall is remarkable, my dear fellow. Yes and I believe he carried out experiments on a number of people, not to mention the family cat, before death resulted in one of them, I forget which. Thallium is a heavy metal and its salts are used in a variety of industrial processes and at one time as a pesticide, even to this day in Eastern European countries.'

'No chance, then, that it could have been taken by accident?'

'None at all in an urban domestic situation like this. The chemical is not one you just find lying about and strict security measures have to be taken in its industrial use.'

'Is there no treatment for it?'

'Yes, there is. The chemical has the unprepossessing name of potassium ferri-hexacyanoferrate, or for the chemically illiterate, Prussian blue, but for it to have an effect, obviously the diagnosis has to be made and soon at that.'

'And it wasn't?'

'No, it wasn't made at all. To be fair, though, the early symptoms are non-specific and it is only later, when the patients develop

12

peripheral neuritis and loss of hair that the penny drops and, I have to say, not always then, either.'

★ ★ ★

After they had dropped Tyrrell back at the Yard, the two detectives went to St Gregory's Hospital, but apart from learning the address of the gambling club, from which the ambulance crew had picked Kate Farrant up, they obtained very little further information than they hadn't already gleaned from Tredgold. The woman who had come to visit her the day after her admission (but was not allowed to do so as the patient was so ill) was evidently in the patient's employ and had let the ambulance crew into the building, but she had little to tell the authorities at the hospital other than that Miss Farrant had seemed in her normal good health earlier that evening and that she hadn't any knowledge of her next of kin.

Their next visit was to the gambling club, which was in a large detached house only a short walk from South Kensington underground station. It had a separate garage at the side with its gates flush with the fence protecting the property from the pavement. The house was set back several yards from the high fence, which together with a screen of large shrubs and trees almost entirely hid its facade.

There was a highly polished brass plate by the side of the metal gate leading to the front door of the building with 'The Spinning Wheel Club' inscribed on it in small letters and a bell push and a microphone above it.

'Please come in, I'll be waiting for you at the front door,' the disembodied voice replied, when Sinclair had identified himself and Sarah.

There was a short flight of stone steps leading up to the front door of the house, which Sinclair thought probably dated from the late eighteenth century and might well have been designed by Nash. The woman who greeted them was of medium height, wearing a white shirt and a navy blue skirt and had jet-black hair and dark brown eyes.

'I'm Jill Corsie,' she said, shaking the detectives' hands and giving them a smile, 'and as I explained on the phone, I am the manager here. Shall we go into my office?' Once they were inside the room, the woman made a gesture towards the chair in front of the desk. 'Cup of tea or coffee?'

Sinclair shook his head. 'No, thank you. As I told you on the telephone, we always look into the reasons for an unexplained death, particularly when we know that the person in question had not seen their doctor in the recent past. You were good enough to tell us the name of the private general practitioner who attends this club when required and he informed us that Miss Farrant had never consulted him personally and had always appeared to be in robust good health.'

'Yes, I can vouch for that, too.'

'There will have to be a post-mortem examination and an inquest, in due course, and in the meantime, we are making some preliminary enquiries. Miss Farrant's death must have come as a great shock to you.'

The woman nodded. 'It has indeed and I am still trying to work out what to do about it. You see, Miss Farrant inherited the club from her late father and I am unaware of any next of kin. There may be some further information in her flat, but, apart from getting some contract cleaners to deal with the mess in there, I didn't feel it was my place to look for any personal papers, particularly as I found that the door to her study was locked in the same way as the entrance to the flat from the lobby — that is, with a key pad.'

'Why did she do that if the flat was locked securely anyway?' asked Sarah.

'Miss Farrant guarded her privacy very carefully, unlike her father, who was very outgoing and friendly, and I don't think she trusted anyone all that much. Mrs Grant the housekeeper here had access to most of the flat, but not even she was allowed to go into the study.'

'How long have you been here yourself?' asked Sinclair.

'Nearly five years now. I was appointed by Mr Richard Farrant, Kate's father. I saw the advertisement and as I had office management experience at my previous job, I decided to put in for it as I wanted to come down to London.'

'Where was your place of work?'

'Basingstoke.'

'Quite a change for you, then?'

'Yes, but I have been enjoying it.'

'I know that this is a gambling club,' Sarah said, 'but what sort of clientele does it have?'

'Very select and both Mr Farrant and his daughter were most particular about that. Every candidate had to be proposed by an existing member and then interviewed by a small panel, which usually consisted of Mr Farrant himself and two other senior members.'

'Wasn't Mr Farrant killed in a powerboat race in the USA?'

'Yes, that was in 2005 and came as a terrible shock. He was a very charismatic person and everybody liked him.'

'What about his daughter?'

'She was very different. One mustn't speak ill of the dead, but although she was frighteningly efficient in all she did — she was also in the chair of The Frampton Trust, which provides funds for research into Alzheimer's disease and helps sufferers from it — she completely lacked his charm and friendly attitude to everyone.'

'Did Mr Farrant have a wife and any other children?'

'He was a widower and did have a son, Adam, but he went missing, believed killed in Iraq a couple of years ago.'

'That family hasn't had much luck, has it? What do you think is likely to happen to this club now?' asked Sarah.

'Well, what with the awful mess downstairs and having to get specialist cleaners in, I decided to close it down, at least for the time being. Had Miss Farrant been in a fit state, I would have consulted her about what to do about it, but she wasn't and as I gathered from what little the hospital people would tell me that she was getting steadily worse and not fit for any visitors, I decided to act on my own initiative and close it down at least until it became clear how long she was likely to be away. The terrible news of her death naturally changed all that.'

'So what is the situation now?'

'I am in the process of arranging a meeting of the group of the senior members, who used to join Miss Farrant from time to time if there were any appointments of new croupiers or policy decisions to make, and get their advice. Obviously, Miss Farrant's will is bound to have an important bearing on the club's future and I have already contacted the club's solicitor, who has agreed to take part in the discussions as well. However, Miss Farrant employed a different solicitor for her personal affairs and we are hoping that he or she will get in touch with us soon, now that the notice of her death has been in the newspapers. Unfortunately I don't know his or her name.'

'When was the last time you saw Miss Farrant before she was taken ill?' Sinclair asked.

'During the afternoon of the day before it happened. Whenever she was in residence here, she always used to put in a brief appearance in the club from time to time to ensure that everything was as it should be. I didn't see her after that until the ambulance men arrived and I can't be sure that she didn't go out during the evening, but if she did, it should have been picked up on the security camera outside the main door to her

18

flat at the back of the building.'

'And did she seem her usual self that afternoon?'

'Yes.'

'Do you have a security officer here?'

'Yes, we do.' The woman glanced at her watch. 'He should be in about now. He checks the security system, clocks in the croupiers and stewards as they arrive and then keeps a general eye on things during the evening, finally making sure that everything is in order after everyone has left.'

'What time is that?'

'The club closes at midnight and usually all the staff have gone by 12.45. The croupiers have to change and the housekeeper then sees them off the premises.'

'Does she live in?'

'Yes. Like me, she also has a flat on the top floor.'

'How long has the club been running?' Sarah asked.

'It was started by Kate's grandfather soon after the war and then Richard Farrant took it over about twenty years ago.'

'And he appointed you as secretary here?'

'That's right. He was extremely good-looking — you may have noticed the rather striking portrait of him in the hall.'

'I can't say that I did. Perhaps you'd show

it to us when we look round.'

'Would you mind if I left that to the security officer and our housekeeper as there have been a great many calls and letters and I really ought to get on with them?'

'I quite understand. I'll have a word with him myself and Inspector Prescott will see the housekeeper. Perhaps you'd be good enough to introduce us. By the way, our men will be coming to take a look at the flat downstairs later today and in the meantime we don't want anyone to go in there. Perhaps you'd let me have any keys to it in your possession.'

'I don't have any. As I said, Mrs Grant knows the number of the entry pad on the door from the lobby, but Miss Farrant kept both keys to the outside and the number of the pad on her study door herself.'

'What about fire regulations?'

'I asked her about that and she told me that there was a key to the main entrance to the flat from the garden side of the building at the local fire station.'

'Bit unusual that, isn't it?' asked Sarah.

'I thought so, too, but she was not someone who took kindly to what she might have thought was either intrusion or idle curiosity.'

★ ★ ★

20

Phyllis Grant was a stout, comfortable-looking woman in her late fifties and after they had been introduced, she took Sarah up to the second floor in the lift.

'You must have found Miss Farrant's death extremely upsetting.'

The woman nodded 'Yes, I did, and I haven't come to terms with it at all. It's funny in a way. I didn't like her at all and yet now this has happened, I . . . '

'Why didn't you like her?'

'Well, I suppose it had a lot to do with the fact that I both respected and, much more than that, loved, her father, Richard.' The woman smiled. 'I mean that in the old-fashioned sense of the word; I assure you it had nothing to do with sex. He always had a smile and a pleasant word with everyone here, whoever they were, and people looked upon it as an honour to serve him and this club and do the best they could.'

'And Kate Farrant wasn't like that?'

The woman raised her eyebrows. 'You see, Richard trusted people and inevitably the odd person took advantage of it, but there was no possibility of anyone taking advantage of Kate. The croupiers are paid very well here and it is a rule that they are never to accept tips and presents. It is a sensible rule as one can't have any hint of corruption or cheating

21

in a place like this, but the odd compliment from a punter, or even flowers or a Christmas cake and champagne to be shared by them during the festive season never did any harm and Richard always attended that sort of party and in addition provided that sort of appreciation for everyone's hard work himself. That goes down well, particularly if it is carried off with sincerity and no hint of pomposity and he didn't make a song and dance out of it, either. Kate would have none of it and was utterly ruthless. She told me that everyone was very well paid and that the conditions here were excellent, so why should they expect anything extra? It's not that she was ever unfair, but any infraction of the rules and that person was out. Our previous security man was a typical example. He was having a quiet smoke out in the back garden when he was on duty and he was out straight away and no argument. There was another incident, too, only a few months back and I never got to the bottom of that one.'

'What sort of incident?' asked Sarah.

'One of the croupiers, her name was Cathy Prior, had only been here about three months when, out of the blue, Miss Farrant told me that she had decided to leave. Naturally, I asked her why and all she would say was that the girl had decided that she wasn't suited for the work and wanted to go. It didn't make sense to me. Cathy was young for her age and a bit silly at times, but she seemed happy enough to me and was clearly enjoying the job. I have to say that she looked more than a bit tarty the very first time she came in to work — I'm sure you know the sort of thing, braless and skirt more than halfway up her thighs — but she only did it once. I explained that what she did away from the club was nothing to do with me, but once she came in through the gate she was at work and the dress code had been pointed out to her at her interview. I told her that she would have to go back home and change into something more sensible and if she did so, that would be the last thing she heard about it.'

'And it worked?'

'It seemed so, even though on one occasion she came out of the showers and walked straight into the big room where they all put on their make-up and, stark naked, sat down and started to do hers. I suppose she thought that it was just a bit of a joke and when I tackled her about it, she just said that a lot of the others were stuck up and stuffy and need 'to get a life', as she put it.'

'Did she do anything like that again?'

'No, she didn't. The senior girl there told her to grow up and if she did anything like it again, she'd warm her backside with her hairbrush. Apart from that she pointed out that Kate Farrant used to go up there unannounced from time to time to see that everything was in order and if she caught her fooling around like that, she'd be out on her ear.

'I don't know whether she believed that or not, but she certainly never risked fooling about like that again, at least not to my knowledge. There's no doubt, though, that if Miss Farrant had heard about it, let alone caught her in the act, the girl would have been dismissed just like that. Naturally I wondered if she had blotted her copybook with Miss Farrant in some way or other later on and perhaps that's why she decided to leave. I did ask Miss Corsie about it, but she was as puzzled as I was.'

'What role does Miss Corsie play in the control of the staff?'

'She deals with the pay for all of us, controls the staff other than the croupiers, who are my responsibility, and liaised with Miss Farrant over any issues involving the members, the building and the grounds. She's also always on hand to smooth things over if anything goes wrong and I remember once that she dealt with one of the girls with whom I was having a bit of trouble. Some time back, it must have been about a year ago, one of them wasn't taking enough care with her personal hygiene and there's no excuse for that as the facilities in their rest area are excellent. I had a word with her and she was extremely rude back. I haven't the power to sack anyone, so I spoke to Miss Corsie about it.

'She was very calm but very firm and without once raising her voice told the girl that no one was forcing her to work here but that we expected high standards of personal cleanliness. She pointed out that all the staff were given everything needed for that purpose here, even if that was not true of her circumstances at home. She finished by saying that the choice was hers, if what she had said was not acceptable, then Miss Farrant would be informed and she had little doubt that that would lead to her dismissal. She finished by saying that the language used to her would not be tolerated, either, and any repeat of that would have the same result.'

'Did it work?'

'It did and it didn't. The girl let out a torrent of swear words and stomped out of Miss Corsie's office and was promptly dismissed. There are no flies on Miss Corsie; she had recorded their conversation and explained to me that one had to cover one's back in situations like that as no-win no-fee solicitors are only too available and the club needed to be very careful about that sort of thing.'

'She sounds very organized.'

'She is and never leaves anything to chance; that's why she was so good with Miss Farrant.'

'What about personal relationships?'

'If you ask me, she doesn't have any. She is always polite to me, but even after living in the next flat to her for a number of years, I don't know the first thing about her personal life.'

'Was Miss Farrant away a lot?'

'Yes, quite frequently, but never for very long and Miss Corsie was always able to contact her by telephone if there was any sort of crisis, which there very seldom was.'

'What about Miss Farrant's flat? Did she look after it herself?' asked Sarah.

'No, I used to go down there every morning after she had her breakfast to make her bed, clean the bathroom and stock her fridge. She very much valued her privacy and although I knew the combination of the lock on the door to her flat from the hall, I would never go down at any other time, unless she asked me to.'

'Did Mr Farrant also live in the basement

flat when he was alive?'

'Yes, but only when he was in London, which wasn't very often. He also had a family house in Buckinghamshire, but that was sold and after that we saw rather more of him although he spent a lot of time abroad, particularly the USA, where he did most of his powerboat racing. The flat downstairs is quite large and has a separate entrance from the garden at the back.'

'I gather that he was killed in an accident.'

'Yes, it was terrible. The boat did a complete somersault and both Mr Farrant and his co-pilot were dead when the rescue launch came on the scene. I saw it all on the television news.'

On the next floor, where they got out of the lift, Sarah was shown into a large sitting-room, with easy chairs and a water cooler and a coffee machine on one side and leading off that, an even larger dressing room for the croupiers. Against one of its walls was a long shelf containing drawers with a mirror along its whole length and stools set in front of it.

'Does each croupier have her own place and drawer?' Sarah asked.

'Oh, yes.'

'The young women are certainly very well looked after,' she said, smiling at the woman. 'What about toilet facilities?'

'They are through that door there.'

'May I have a look?'

'Of course.'

'I'm most impressed,' Sarah said, after she had been shown the basins, lavatories, three walk-in shower cubicles and the neat pile of fluffy towels. 'I'm sure the women must appreciate it.'

'Most of them do, but you get the odd one who's a bit stroppy and leaves her stuff all over the place, but they only do that once. I won't have it and neither will Miss Corsie and I can tell you if she tells them off, they don't do anything she doesn't like again unless they want to be shown the door.'

'She sounds a bit of a gorgon.'

'You could say that, but if you follow her rules — and she's often up here checking on the girls' appearance before they go down — she's fine. At least you know exactly where you are with her and if you think she might be a gorgon, you really needed to see Miss Farrant.'

★ ★ ★

'You been in the force?' Sinclair asked, when he had been introduced to the security officer, Bert Powell by Miss Corsie and the woman had gone back into her office.

The man grinned. 'Is it that obvious? Yes, I was a sergeant in the uniform branch. I saw this job advertised and with my June not being in the best of health, the hours suited me better and I jumped at it — I don't have to get here until eleven.'

'Like it here, do you?'

'Gets a bit dull at times, but madam kept us all up to the mark.'

'What exactly do you have to do?'

'Check that everything in the gaming rooms is as it should be, that the toilets down here have been properly cleaned and that the towels have been changed. Then I make sure that all the monitors and recorders are properly set up and then check in the members as they arrive, usually from about four onwards. After that, I wander around keeping an eye on things, making sure that the girls aren't being hassled, that the punters are not drinking excessively, are behaving and watching out for anyone losing too much.'

'What about the housekeeper, Mrs Grant? Do you get on well with her?'

'Yeah, she's a good sort — nice friendly woman and good with the girls. She's also the only one ever allowed into Miss Farrant's flat. She goes in there to clean up the bathroom and make the bed when the boss is in residence.'

'I'd be interested to see the set-up down here and in the gaming rooms. Perhaps you'd be good enough to show me? The flat will have to wait until our men have finished there.'

'Right.'

The man pointed to a door at the side of the hall. 'There's a large cloakroom for the members through there and next to it is the kitchen. Proper meals are not provided, but we do have a steward who prepares light snacks there; the drinks are also stored there except those locked up in the bar upstairs, which the steward serves during opening hours — you can see the lift over there. That door leads to Miss Farrant's flat in the basement; it also has a separate entrance from the garden at the rear of the building.'

On the first floor was the main gaming area in which roulette, blackjack, baccarat and poker were played and there was also a bar at one end and two other doors leading to two small rooms for the serious poker players.

'You no doubt have TV surveillance. Are those two rooms covered as well?'

'Oh, yes, and all the images are recorded in the room through that door there. If I spot any potential trouble and I don't want to make my presence too obvious, then I can watch a particular table on the monitor.'

'What about the outside?'

'There are three cameras, which cover the main and side entrances and the door to the basement flat, which is at the rear of the building, all of which run the whole time.'

'Was that the case the night Miss Farrant was taken ill?'

'Yes.'

'And do you still have the tapes?'

'Yes. If anything out of the ordinary happens, I keep them until such time as the incident has been cleared up.'

'Has there been any trouble recently?'

'Well, there was an incident involving a girl a few months back. She hadn't been here for more than a few weeks and I had my eye on her, because she was more up front and younger than the usual run of croupiers.' The man grinned. 'I mean up front in more ways than one. Unlike the others, she always had a cheeky smile for everyone and also liked to show rather more of her assets, which were quite considerable. I did warn her once that Miss Farrant didn't like that sort of thing and that she was getting more than a bit too close to the mark.'

'What was her reaction?' asked Sinclair.

'She just gave me a grin and a wiggle and said: 'Don't be an old fuddy-duddy, Bert.' Anyway, I was wandering around near the roulette wheel and I noticed a bloke giving her a bit of the eye. She quite clearly was well aware of it and I saw her raise her eyebrows and give him the suspicion of a wink. I didn't pay all that much attention to it, but enough to keep on the lookout when the man came to the club again the following week and again a few days later.

'It didn't take long for me to be sure that there was more than a little gentle flirtation going on. One evening, I saw him give her bum a squeeze as he went past her. It was over in a second and he obviously thought that no one had seen, but the girl's reaction made it clear to me that she was aroused rather than outraged by what he had done and I was watching the monitor which was focused on the side entrance that the girls used when they left at the end of the evening. He was there, waiting for her, and their embrace was, how shall I put it, distinctly enthusiastic.

'I was a bit torn about drawing it to Miss Farrant's attention, because I didn't want to get the girl, Cathy Prior, into trouble unnecessarily, but at the same time, she was younger than the rest of them and I was concerned about her. Better for her to lose her job than get into a mess with a bloke old enough to be her father, I thought. My mind was made up when I went through the book I have, which contains photographs and names of all the members. It was when I discovered that the man, one Rupert Chester, who is in his forties, is married and a QC, that I decided to show the tape to Miss Farrant.'

'How did Miss Farrant react?'

'Just thanked me for my vigilance and said that she'd deal with the situation. I don't know what that amounted to, except that, soon after, she told me to remove his entry from the book, because the man was no longer a member.'

'Did you keep the tape in question?'

'Yes, I know enough about incidents like this to be very careful and before giving the original to Miss Farrant, I made a copy of it.'

'Right. I'd like to take a look at it myself and perhaps you'd make another copy for me to take away.'

'Yes, I can do that for you.'

When he looked at the tape, Sinclair could see why the security man had been alerted by Chester's behaviour at the roulette table. He was sitting on the other side of the table to Cathy Prior, his eyes fixed on her, hardly even glancing in the direction of the roulette wheel as it went round, unlike everyone else, whose gaze was centred on it. If the girl was aware of what he was doing, she showed no sign of it, ignoring not only him but everyone else playing. When he finally got up, he paused for a moment behind her, looked down over her shoulders, raised his eyebrows slightly and then moved away.

The camera outside the building picked the girl up directly she came out of the side door. She gave a broad smile to someone ahead of her, then ran into the man's arms, giving him a distinctly enthusiastic and prolonged kiss, and then the two of them turned and walked away.

'How did a man like that manage to get into the club? From what you have said about Miss Farrant, he seems to have been the last person one would have expected to be tolerated by her.'

'I mustn't exaggerate, he behaved perfectly well apart from his attitude to the girl. He didn't drink too much, he didn't plunge too heavily at the tables and he was always polite to me and QCs have their contacts. She may have thought that one of them might be of use in her charitable work.'

'Do you know if Miss Corsie got involved in all this?'

'No, I don't, but I imagine so. After all, she was the one in charge on the ground a lot of the time and I wouldn't have thought that

Miss Farrant would have left her in the dark about it.'

'Do you have any follow-up information about either the man or the girl after they were kicked out?'

The man shook his head. 'I took a good look at the daily papers that are taken here and saw nothing about them at all.'

'Do you check the members in yourself when they arrive?'

'Yes, I do, and they have to show their membership card each time, whoever they are and however well I know them.'

'And those two haven't shown their faces since?'

'No and if they had, I'd have sent them packing, I can tell you.'

'Old instincts still alive, then?'

The man grinned. 'Once a copper, always a copper. At least that's what they say.'

'Did Miss Farrant allude to the incident again?'

'No, she didn't.'

'Have you still got the tapes for the night Miss Farrant was taken ill?'

'Yes.'

'And have you had a look at them yet?'

'Yes and they merely showed the ambulance people trying to get a response from the door to the flat at the rear of the building and then them carrying her out through the front one.'

'Well, perhaps you'd let me have copies of those tapes focused on all three doors from the time you set the recordings up until the ambulance men came. I'd like our people to take a look at them.'

'All right.'

'How did you get on with the woman yourself?'

'Pretty well, but I always thought I was walking on eggshells with her. For what it's worth, I don't think she liked men.'

'In the sense I think you mean?' The man grinned and then nodded. 'How about Miss Corsie?'

'Tarred with the same brush if you ask me.'

'With each other?'

'I'm pretty sure not. Their body language didn't suggest it, at least not to me. I wouldn't be so sure about either Miss Corsie or Miss Farrant with the girls, though; they had that certain way of looking at them. It's not easy to hide that sort of body language.'

'How about the punters? Do they behave themselves?' Sinclair asked.

'Drink is the thing you have to watch with them and those on a bad losing streak. Not, mind you, that the stakes allowed here are that high. In fact, quite a lot of the members come here for the social aspects, to meet other influential people and get away from their wives.'

The man raised his eyebrows and gave Sinclair a smile.

'Do you know if Miss Farrant was in the building the whole evening before she died?'

'She was certainly here in the late afternoon when I saw her, but I don't know about the time after that. If she did go out, it would be recorded on those tapes. There's something dodgy about Miss Farrant's death, isn't there?'

'What makes you say that?'

'Just the old instinct. It stands to reason, don't it? When did two DIs last come to investigate a straightforward stomach upset?'

'Just let me have those tapes, would you, and if you value my advice, keep that sort of speculation firmly under your hat — and don't tell me you don't wear one.'

The man nodded. 'Just as you say, guv. I'll get them for you now.'

'That presumably is Richard Farrant,' Sinclair said, as they walked back through the lobby towards the security man's office and looked up at the picture over the fireplace in the lobby. The man was strikingly good-looking, with thick black hair, and was wearing white overalls and held a crash helmet in his hand.

'That's right. Looks the part, doesn't he? Proper Boys' Own Paper sort of bloke.'

'Read that when you were a lad, did you?'

'Certainly did. Bit before your time, eh, guv?'

'Yes, but my older brother kept a few old copies.'

2

Over a cup of coffee at a restaurant near South Kensington underground station, the two detectives brought each other up to date on what they had discovered.

'He's no fool, that security man, and even making allowances for the fact that he's an ex uniform sergeant, he knew at once that there were suspicious circumstances surrounding Kate Farrant's death,' Sinclair told Sarah. 'He also clocked her and Miss Corsie as being gay, although he reckoned they weren't involved with one another. Thallium is an unusual poison and it must be difficult to get hold of it. I looked it up on the internet before coming here and I understand that symptoms following ingestion come on usually within a few hours and a maximum of forty-eight. In view of the severity of Kate Farrant's initial symptoms, I would put it on the short side of the scale, but I'd have to check that with an expert. If that's true, the poison must have been given to her while she was in the building. How was it administered? That's a tricky one. She clearly wasn't the sort of person to be having a friendly drink with either a staff member or one of the punters. According to Bert Powell, she was in the building when he arrived for work early that afternoon at about 2 p.m. and, as far as he knew, she was still there when he left at about half past midnight. He parks his motorbike by the side of the garage and noticed a light in her flat through one of the windows as he was wheeling it round to the front.'

'What do you suppose is going to happen to the club now?' asked Sarah.

'I imagine that will depend on Kate Farrant's will, if she had made one, and we'll have to see what Jack Pocock and his team find in her flat. At least there should be an address of her solicitor — there must have been a lot of legal ends to tie up when she inherited the club. The scene-of-crime people are bound to take quite a bit of time and clearly we need to visit the Frampton Trust's offices before we brief Tyrrell.'

'Yes. Although it would save time to go separately, I think that there would be advantages for us to go together — it's easier to assess reactions in that way. Why don't we go to the offices first?'

'Good idea.'

* * *

The offices of The Frampton Trust were in a new block in the City and the furnishings were all antiseptic, with angular steel-framed furniture and large plate-glass windows. The chief executive, one Brigadier Forest, was equally antiseptic. Immaculate in his dark suit, stiff collar, regimental tie and black shoes polished to a mirror-like finish, he hardly seemed to Sarah to be full of the milk of human kindness and was somehow out of place in an organization devoted to the support of demented patients.

'Did Miss Farrant have much to do with the day-to-day running of this organization?' Sinclair asked.

The brigadier managed to give the impression that such an ill-informed question was a total irrelevance, but did deign to reply.

'Miss Farrant, as I am sure you know, was in the chair of the board and her sad loss is a bitter blow to our organization. She always kept her finger firmly on the pulse, was always present at the meetings, but she never interfered with the day-to-day running.'

'What about the assessment of those applying for aid?' Sarah asked.

'We have fully trained social workers to help us with that.'

'How are the finances managed?' asked Sinclair.

41

'We have a full-time treasurer, who is a qualified accountant, and banking services and investment advice are supplied free by one of the big banks as their contribution to the charity. The same is true of our auditor.'

'Has it always been like that?'

'No and it was Miss Farrant who insisted on the whole enterprise being put on a professional basis when she took over the chair. In Sir Henry Frampton's day — he founded the trust — it was all done a bit on the 'old boy' network, but she took the view that the organization had moved beyond all that and she was quite right, too.'

'Was she resented as a result?'

'There have been those who think she was too pushy, but they can't gainsay what has been achieved since her arrival on the scene and she made it clear that being on the board was a privilege and if there was anyone who didn't view it in that light, resignation was always an option.'

'But you are not one of them?'

The man raised his eyebrows. 'Do you think I would work here if I was?'

'How long have you been chief executive?'

'I was appointed just over a year ago, some six months after Sir Henry Frampton's death, soon after Miss Farrant had succeeded him as chairperson.'

42

'And whom did you succeed?'

'My post was a new one. Ever since the charity was founded by Sir Henry, it had been run on a fairly informal basis; Sir Henry was chairman and he, with a Miss Nanson, who had a background in social work, dealt with the applications for grants. His son Paul, with the help of a Miss Fisher, was in charge of fundraising and publicity. There was no board as such and about a year before his death, when he was already ill, Sir Henry decided that the organization needed to be put on a more formal footing. As a result, Miss Farrant became chairperson elect, I was appointed as chief executive and we also have a professional fundraiser, who has back-up staff. Paul Frampton resigned before I took up my appointment and Miss Farrant made it clear that he had severed all connection with the charity.'

'What about financial direction?'

'Miss Farrant, who was a chartered accountant, was looking into the finances at Sir Henry's request after the previous treasurer, who was a friend of the chairman, became incapacitated by a stroke and as a result the whole organization was restructured and for reasons that I was not party to, Miss Fisher was not retained and Mr Paul Frampton decided to resign his position.'

'Do you know why he did that?'

'It happened before my time and I saw no reason to pursue the matter. Miss Farrant told me that a line had been drawn under the matter and that it was closed. If you had met Miss Farrant, Inspector, you would understand that she was not the sort of person to tolerate discussion about past decisions on which agreement had been reached. She was a most efficient chairperson and under her leadership, the charity was going from strength to strength.' The man suddenly shifted his gaze and looked unblinkingly at Sinclair for a moment or two. 'May I enquire if there was anything unusual about Miss Farrant's death?'

'Why do you ask?'

'The police, let alone two inspectors from Scotland Yard, don't normally call about any ordinary illness, now do they?'

'It wasn't an ordinary illness, that's the whole point. These days, previously perfectly healthy young women don't often die within a few days of a mysterious malady, which defied diagnosis while she was alive. The fact that she was well known makes it even more imperative that we are thorough about looking into the circumstances.'

That was as far as they were able to get with the brigadier, but through his secretary, they succeeded in obtaining the addresses and phone numbers of Paul Frampton and Miss Nanson. The young woman clearly knew nothing about either Kate Farrant or the past history of the organization.

'Do you have photographs of Mr Paul Frampton and Miss Fisher? If so, I would like copies' Sinclair said.

The young woman flushed. 'I'd have to ask the brigadier and I'm not sure that . . . '

'I expect you've heard the expression 'obstructing the police in the course of their enquiries' and I hardly think it necessary to worry the brigadier with a simple request like that and if you're that worried I won't mention it to him.'

Sinclair looked very directly at the young woman, who glanced anxiously in Sarah's direction as if wanting support, but when that had clearly failed, pressed her lips together and turned towards a large filing cabinet.

'Well, there are some publicity shots of them which were taken at a polo match that was organized for the charity by Miss Fisher and . . . '

'They would do very nicely, thank you.'

While she was getting out the file, the young woman kept shooting anxious glances at the door to the brigadier's office and her relief when she had handed the photos across

and the two detectives turned to leave was
only too obvious.

★ ★ ★

Margaret Nanson lived in Beckenham. She
invited the two detectives in for a cup of
tea. She looked to be in her early sixties and
was plump, softly spoken and had a ready
smile.

'I am sorry to have to spring this on you
just like that,' Sarah said, 'but we are
enquiring into the sad death of Kate Farrant
and didn't think it fair to do so on the phone.
I am sure you understand that when a
prominent person dies at such a young age
and after such a short illness we have to look
into the circumstances, particularly when the
press start raising all sorts of hares.'

They both could see at once that the
woman was not entirely convinced by what
Sarah had said, but was too polite to question
it.

'Yes, I did read about it in the paper and
was very shocked by the news. You see, her
father and grandfather knew Sir Henry well
and inevitably I had some contact with both
Kate and her brother Adam, during all the
years I spent working for Sir Henry. Indeed, I
still feel almost part of the charity even

though I have nothing directly to do with it now.'

'We have, of course, already been to the club in South Kensington, which Miss Farrant owned,' Sinclair told her, 'but we are also interested in her involvement with The Frampton Trust and the brigadier we met at the headquarters wasn't able to tell me much about it prior to his appointment as chief executive.'

The woman smiled. 'That I can well imagine. He left me in no doubt when I met him during the takeover that he thought that the whole business was amateurish and needed 'a new and strong hand at the helm'.'

'As I said, the circumstances surrounding Miss Farrant's illness are not clear and we are trying to find out as much about her as we can, hence our visit,' said Sarah. 'So far, we have not discovered if she has any close relatives with whom she kept in contact and are wondering if you know anything about that. You see, apart from anything else, there is the important matter of tracing her next of kin.'

'Why don't I get us a cup of tea and I will try to get my thoughts together?'

Several minutes went by while the woman busied herself in the kitchen getting the tea, and when she brought it through and poured it out she sat down opposite them.

'I never liked Adam and Kate Farrant. You see, I knew them both when they were children. In their different ways, they were very pleased with themselves. I was the social worker who worked with the family when Sir Henry and his wife lived quite near the Farrants in Buckinghamshire. Lady Frampton had recently been diagnosed as having Alzheimer's disease and then, when she gradually became more seriously affected, Sir Henry asked me if I would become her resident companion and helper. I liked them both, I was becoming disenchanted with the organization of the social services with the endless form-filling and nitpicking bureaucracy, and he was offering me my keep and more pay, so I agreed to take the job on. My previous experience meant that I was able to organize all the various aids she needed and did my best to stimulate her interest in as many activities as possible. She was such a nice woman and she never became aggressive or unpleasant in the way that some of those patients do. As to Sir Henry, he was a rather gruff man, but his heart was most definitely in the right place. It is not everyone, even if money is no problem, who would have kept his wife at home, particularly when she became incontinent, we had to employ a full-time nurse and she hardly seemed to know her husband. Whenever he was there, he would spend a lot of time sitting by the bed and reading to her, although latterly he knew she wasn't able to understand. He told me that he thought that she recognized his voice and that it might give her some comfort to hear it.

'It was when Lady Frampton died some ten years ago, after which he slipped into a deep depression, that I suggested the idea of his setting up a trust to support those looking after relatives suffering from dementia. To start with, he resisted the idea, but gradually came round to it and took it up with enthusiasm. Knowing that I had had secretarial experience before I moved on to social work, he asked me both to manage the office and to assist in the assessment of patients and their families who applied for grants. The venture took some time to get going, but gradually it began to take off. The scope of the organization increased to include research grants and with that fundraising became important — and that is when Paul Frampton and Jane Fisher came in.

'Paul, Sir Henry's only child, should never have gone into the organization. He had a good degree from Cambridge University in modern languages but had quite the wrong personality for fundraising. He lacks the social skills, being no good with people, and he is a great bear of a man, untidy in appearance and, worst of all, doesn't believe that patients with untreatable dementia should be kept alive, seemingly, as he put it, almost indefinitely. As for Jane, she was nice-looking rather than really pretty and I couldn't see what men saw in her. It wasn't as if she was flirtatious or dressed provocatively, but they seemed to make a beeline for her and it was obvious that she didn't like that at all. She was very good at organizing events, though. Charity balls, polo matches and concerts, you name them, she managed them and she obviously enjoyed mixing with the rich and famous. Worst of all, though, she was not entirely honest.'

'In what way?' asked Sinclair, suddenly very interested.

'She was distinctly free with the petty cash and the accounting in the charity was sloppy in the extreme. An old business partner of Sir Henry, who was a chartered accountant, looked after the books and did the audits and while he may have been good in his day, he was well past it, particularly after he had some minor strokes, or transient ischaemic attacks, as they like to call them these days. Jane managed to persuade Paul to sign

50

cheques and then filled them in herself, many of them for cash. Eventually, she did it once too often, and the accountant, in one of his lucid periods, picked it up and Sir Henry went ballistic.'

'Who appointed her?' asked Sarah.

'I imagine it must have been Sir Henry. Even though he wasn't at all well by then with the leukaemia that was to kill him later, he liked to feel that he was still in control.'

'Did Paul Frampton keep a close eye on the finances?'

'No. He was quite often away giving talks about the aims of the organization and if Jane was arranging a ball or a reception, she had to settle bills when he wasn't in the office. I'm not quite sure what arrangements were made, but I remember once he signed a blank cheque when he was off somewhere and asked me to give it to Jane.'

'That wasn't very wise, was it?'

'No, I don't suppose it was, but he obviously trusted Jane and, anyway, he was certainly no businessman. I've always felt rather sorry for him.'

'Why was that?'

'Sir Henry used to talk to me a lot when his wife got so bad and I think he felt, personally, that he was born at the wrong time. He was a very patriotic man. He often told me how much he regretted having just missed service in the Second World War and he was a great supporter of the Falklands campaign. And then there were games. Although he wasn't all that good at them, he very much enjoyed golf and tennis and would have liked to share them with Paul, who was a great disappointment to him in that regard. Paul was overweight as a child, lacked coordination and any games, particularly contact sports, were an utter misery to him, not helped by the fact that he had to wear glasses.

'The whole thing was aggravated when Sir Henry bought a property near the Farrants in Buckinghamshire. Walter Farrant took a liking to Sir Henry and used to invite him over to his property. Walter's grandchildren, Adam and Kate, were just the sort of young people that Sir Henry liked and admired. They were bright, good at games and physically active, swimming like fish in the outdoor pool and riding furiously in the grounds. And then there was Richard, Walter's son and the father of the twins. He became a widower when they were babies, and at that time was something of a national hero, with his exploits in powerboats. He was everything that Sir Henry would have liked in a son of his own, being extremely good-looking, a talented all-round sportsman and a thoroughly nice man, and Sir Henry admired him greatly. To be honest, I fancied him myself and me a desiccated old spinster! He ran a gambling club in London, but the children always came down to the country house during the school holidays.

'Sir Henry also felt very much the same about Richard Farrant's son, Adam, who, like his father, was exceptionally good-looking, an excellent games player, being in the army cricket and squash sides, and a heroic soldier, who had served with distinction in Northern Ireland and then in Iraq. He also knew how to handle Sir Henry, listening to his stories and always being deferential. As for Kate, she was extremely clever, she got a first-class degree in chemistry at University College, and she was also very direct and efficient in everything she did.

'Paul is not made of wood and I am sure you can imagine how hurt he must have been when his father kept on comparing him unfavourably with the Farrant children, not least when Kate swept in, and the last straw was when she was made chairperson of the charity.'

'Was Sir Henry's money inherited?'

'No, it wasn't. Someone told me that he was involved in property development soon after the end of the war and there were hints by some of the people I met in relation to the charity that he was involved in shady dealings in his early days in the property market, but I didn't believe them. He was a great supporter of various other charities for many years and that was how he gained a knighthood.

'Sir Henry obviously admired the Farrants, but he must also have had concerns about the way the finances were being run to have asked Kate to look into them. I think the reason was that he didn't want to make it too obvious and embarrass Paul, which is why he turned to her rather than employ a firm of accountants. I think he must also have been unaware of just how much Paul resented the way his father was always praising her and her brother. Did you ever meet Kate Farrant?'

'No,' said Sinclair.

'Well, as you no doubt have heard she was a very direct person and she must have told Sir Henry that financial control was extremely slack and that it needed to be put on a more formal basis. I can only presume, too, that she must have convinced him that Paul and Jane were not up to the task and when he made his feelings clear, they both resigned as a result.'

'That must have caused a considerable stir and on the face of it that sounds a very

54

extreme reaction, particularly as far as Paul Frampton was concerned. Do you think there was more to it than met the eye?' asked Sarah.

'Yes, I do. I'm pretty sure that his heart was never really in his job with the charity and the concern over the finances may have been the opportunity he was looking for to give it up. I believe he only took it on in the first place because his father put pressure on him.'

'How did Paul and Jane get on?'

'If you ask me, I think he fancied her — that sort of thing is difficult to hide if you are someone like Paul, who is shy and awkward where women are concerned.'

'And she didn't encourage him in any way?'

'The very opposite. She was always scrupulously polite, but still managed to give the impression that she had no interest in him at all in that direction and I think she considered him frivolous and a bit of a joker. He also speaks in a very pedantic and mannered fashion and he was always dressing up, something which she obviously thought was childish and undignified.'

'Can you give me an example?' asked Sinclair.

'Well, he always used to put on full Father Christmas kit at the party we used to give for fundraisers and their children. He also came into the office one day dressed as a gorilla and on another occasion as a sheikh and Jane wasn't amused at all. In fact, she was quite toffee-nosed about the latter, going on about it being racist and that she for one thought the charity was a serious business and not suited to stupid pranks like that. To be honest, Jane didn't have much of a sense of humour, particularly as far as he was concerned, and it must have been particularly hurtful to him because she could be outgoing and vivacious when meeting potential donors.'

Sinclair decided to change the subject. 'I gather Kate Farrant's brother disappeared in Iraq.'

'Yes, he did. As I said earlier, Sir Henry very much admired him and was very cut up when the news came through. What really stung Paul, though, was the way that Adam Farrant used to behave towards Jane whenever he visited the office. It seemed to me that he could hardly keep his eyes off her. I remember once when he was visiting the office and she was showing him some pictures on her laptop of a polo tournament in Windsor Great Park, one of the charity's more successful ventures. He was leaning over her shoulder and his eyes were not fixed on the screen, but were clearly studying and no doubt admiring her cleavage. He must have sensed that I was watching him because he looked up suddenly. Did he blush or was he embarrassed? Not a bit of it! He gave me a wink. If an inexperienced old maid like me was aware of it, then it seems more than likely Paul was as well.'

'Have you any idea how Jane felt about him?'

'I think she was embarrassed by him and yet didn't seem to know how to give him the brush-off. It was the same when she met men in public. She was polite and friendly, but if ever one of them tried to take it a bit further than that the shutters came down.'

'How did the two men get on together?'

'They were always civil to one another in my presence, but I can't believe they had any interests in common. I mustn't exaggerate, though, about Adam and Jane. He probably behaved like that with a lot of attractive young women and make no mistake about it, Jane was physically attractive all right, and I don't suppose that there was anything more to it than that. Anyway, Paul can't have disliked him too much, because before Adam went out to Iraq, he lent him his flat for a couple of weeks when he was being briefed, or whatever they call it, in London. Paul was away on holiday at the time. One might have expected Adam to have stayed with Kate, but I gather they had some almighty row at one time and were hardly on speaking terms once they left school.'

'The sudden upheaval at the charity must have come as a great shock to you?'

'Yes, it did, particularly the speed with which everything happened after Kate spent time going through the accounts.'

'What about your own position when that happened?'

'Sir Henry asked to see me and I must say I was very touched by what he did. He explained that his dearest wish was to feel that his charity should prosper after he was gone and that he was convinced that the only hope for a secure future was to change the way it was managed completely. Much to his regret, he was convinced that his son Paul was not up to it and that alternative arrangements were already in train. He thanked me for the care I had provided for his wife and all the work I had put in for the charity and said that in recognition for all that he had made arrangements for me to be provided with a generous pension. He died a few weeks after that and the board appointed Kate to succeed him as chairperson.'

'That in itself must have been a bitter blow to Paul.'

'Yes, it would have been much easier for him if someone other than Kate, who was always being praised to the sky by Sir Henry, had taken over and under the circumstances I thought he behaved very well. He delivered the address at his father's memorial service and on the face of it appeared to bear Kate no ill will — I saw them talking to one another at the reception afterwards. The fact that Sir Henry left all his money to the charity didn't mean that Paul was other than comfortably off — his mother, who was wealthy in her own right, bequeathed all that she had to him and his father alluded to that in his will.'

'Do you know what happened to Jane Fisher?'

'No. She was taken ill about the same time as Adam went to Iraq and the trouble blew up over the charity and Kate must have said something to her to the effect that resignation and a quiet departure would be the best thing for everyone concerned.'

'Well, thank you for your help. It has given us a much clearer idea of the set-up at the charity,' Sarah said.

'I do hope you're soon able to clear up the uncertainty over Kate's death. I didn't like her much but I did respect her, and charity donors being fickle animals, publicity and speculation about it will not do the Trust any good.'

'Have you any idea who might take it over?'

'No, but the board has several very distinguished people on it and in due course I'm sure they'll find someone suitable.'

'But it won't be Paul,' Sinclair commented.

'No, I'm quite certain that it won't.'

★ ★ ★

'What did you make of her?' Sarah asked Sinclair when they were on their way to Paul Frampton's flat, having telephoned to make sure that he was in.

'More than a bit holier than thou was my impression. On the face of it she gives the impression of being a benign motherly soul, but she was only too ready, in her quiet way, to put the boot into Paul Frampton, not to mention Jane Fisher, and she obviously didn't like Kate Farrant either, although Adam appears in her estimation just to have been a bit of a Jack the lad. I suspect that she resented her position as Sir Henry Frampton's right-hand woman and confidante being taken away from her.'

'That's a bit harsh, isn't it?'

'Maybe, but it will be interesting to hear what Paul Frampton has to say.'

Paul Frampton was a very large man indeed, not only being tall but also considerably overweight. He had a pair of horn-rimmed glasses hanging by a ribbon from around his neck, which rested on his ample stomach, and when he smiled as he introduced himself to them and shook their hands, his eyes below his bushy eyebrows disappeared almost completely.

'The ever-efficient Jill Corsie at the club rang to tell me that you had been there and to expect a visit, but I have to confess that I didn't anticipate that it would be quite so soon. She's no fool, that woman, and indicated that the police would hardly have been interested if Kate's mysterious illness had been anything straightforward, but she didn't or wouldn't elaborate. This business has a distinct whiff of mystery about it, or so it seems to me. Anyway, before we get involved in the details, how about a drink? On second thoughts, perhaps a cup of coffee would be more appropriate in view of your official visit. Police officers eschew alcohol when on duty, I believe, do they not? At least they do in the crime mysteries I read when I am sated with the dry stuff I usually work on.'

'That is just what I need,' Sinclair replied. 'How about you, Sarah?'

'Me, too.'

'Capital. Sit yourself down while I attend to it.'

As they heard the grinder, Sinclair took the opportunity to look round the sitting room. It was large for that of a flat and contained a three-piece suite, a substantial low-level glass-topped table in the middle, a television set and DVD player in one corner and a music centre in another, and one wall was completely taken up by bookshelves packed with volumes, most of which were reference books.

'Fine room, this,' Sinclair said when the man came back with a tray on which was a coffee pot, a silver jug of cream and a plate with a selection of biscuits on it.

'Yes. People have asked why I didn't take one of the flats with a view, but I'm immune to that sort of blandishment and the complete lack of one doesn't bother me and makes its price marginally less outrageous than many of the others in the block. It's got a very good-sized bedroom and a second one, which not only acts as a study but is large enough to take a single bed for visitors, not that I have any.'

'I see that there's a lot of stuff in French and German in the bookshelves as well as dictionaries of more exotic languages.'

'Yes, I do quite a bit of translating. I am

trying to expand my range and am having a stab at Hungarian at the moment. I was over there for a spell last summer to immerse myself in it; it's not the easiest of languages, I can tell you. You probably know already that I'm otherwise unemployed as the result of 'She-Who-Must-Be-Obeyed's descent on my father's charity like one of the Furies.'

'Yes, I suppose one could describe Ayesha in those terms.'

The man let out a bellow of laughter. 'Touché. Kate would have enjoyed that gentle little put-down, although she would have preferred a more robust delivery. She was always pouring scorn on what she used to refer to as my pretensions of mythological and literary knowledge.'

'It's always gratifying to meet a fellow devotee of Rider Haggard,' Sinclair said.

The man nodded. 'There is one other thing about Kate that I think might amuse you. You see, she had a large colour photograph taken of herself when she was appointed to the chair of the charity and had it put up on the wall of its boardroom. I have a copy and I must show it to you.'

The man disappeared into his study and came back moments later with the picture. Sinclair looked carefully at the image of the young woman with jet-black hair cut in a

1920s style with a fringe just above her dark brown eyes and wearing scarlet lipstick. 'She's certainly very striking looking,' he said, passing the picture across to Sarah, 'and I can't help wondering how she went down with the club members.'

The man chuckled. 'I teased Kate when she had that particular makeover and she didn't take kindly to that at all. She never did have a sense of humour, but she did stick to it despite what I had to say and it certainly caused quite a stir at the club. That was long before the problems with The Frampton Trust blew up.'

'Did she abandon the style later on?'

'No, she stuck to it. I don't blame her. In fact, it suited the image she liked to project of the all-powerful and unattainable woman. There's no doubt, either, that she lived up to it. Always a great one for precision and detail was Kate and it's not surprising that she realized immediately that neither Jane Fisher nor I were up to it within a few hours of sweeping into the charity like a Siberian gale. I mustn't mock her, though, and how she managed to keep the whole thing so quiet, I'll never know. As to Jane, I liked and trusted her and I didn't and don't believe a word that that superficially benign Tiggywinkle of a woman Margaret Nanson hinted at and even accused us of doing. All right, so I was sloppy about the accounting of the petty cash, but the rest of it, which in fact didn't amount to much that wasn't easily put right by Kate, was the responsibility of that demented old has-been that my father insisted on employing as accountant and auditor.'

'If Margaret Nanson was like that, why did your father trust her so completely and arrange for such a generous severance package, if I may put it like that?'

'To be fair, she did an excellent job as far as the care of my mother was concerned, but then as my father began to lose his edge she started to take control of him in various subtle and not so subtle ways. She even began to claim that the charity had been her idea in the first place and that she suggested it to jerk my father out of his depression. That was a load of codswallop; depression was not and never had been a facet of his personality and the charity was his idea and no one else's. Much as I disliked Kate in many ways, if it hadn't been for her, I believe my father might well have left the Nanson woman a great deal of money and it's more than likely that the charity would have folded completely. Of course, I was a great deal to blame for the situation myself. I never wanted to have anything to do with it and if I'd had more backbone, I would have stood up to him and refused to give in to his wish that I should keep the flag flying after he had gone. You mustn't be deceived by my flippant attitude. What has happened and not least Kate Farrant's death has come as a great shock to me. Obviously, though, you never met my father. You see, it was very difficult to say no to him and the fact that he had a potentially fatal illness didn't make it any easier. There's no point in mincing words — the man was a bully and there was no one to control him once my mother began to deteriorate. You've no doubt already discovered that she died from the effects of Alzheimer's disease.'

Sinclair nodded. 'Were you responsible for appointing Jane Fisher?'

'I was a member of the appointment committee and my father was in the chair. He was very impressed by her; she had had a good university education, previous experience in fundraising and organizing functions and good references. She was streets ahead of the other candidates and I was quite happy to see her in the job.'

'And you don't believe that she had her hand in the till?'

'No, I'm quite sure that she hadn't. As I said, financial control was slack and most of that was my fault in not making it quite clear to my father that his old friend, who was supposed to be in charge of it, was senile and incompetent. In any case, it didn't take Kate all that long to sort it all out and I must say this for her, she didn't make a meal of it and somehow managed to keep the full extent of the chaotic management of the finances from the old man. Of course, Kate being Kate, she had a grand plan for the future and persuaded my father that in order to secure it and indeed expand, it needed a properly constituted board to manage it and that it would be best to start with a clean slate.

'She informed my father that Jane had decided to leave and that it was time to put the charity's finances under much stricter control. She also told me, brutally directly as always, that I should have picked up what was happening and that I had two options, either to resign myself, or for my father to be told both about what had happened and my shortcomings with regard to financial control. Needless to say I took a different view of the whole business and thought that what she was saying was unfair. I had had nothing to do with handling the finances; my role was to give talks to influential people about the scourge of Alzheimer's, the fact that the incidence was increasing with the ageing population and the state of research into the condition. Of course I also explained that to achieve improvements in patient management and foster research, large amounts of money were required.'

'And yet although you had no control of the finances, your signature was required on all the cheques?'

'Yes and I have no reason to believe that Jane fiddled them. Jane set up dinners, cocktail parties and presentations and all of that necessitated large amounts of money to be paid out and as I was away a lot, the creditors wouldn't have been prepared to wait too long.'

'I was given to understand that her dishonesty amounted to more than just the odd bit of loose change.'

'I don't know who gave you that idea, although I can guess. You haven't been talking to Margaret Nanson by any chance, have you? Her nose was thoroughly put out of joint when Jane was appointed.'

'I gather, too, that the treasurer was both past it and incompetent.'

'Yes, I'm sure she was right about that and one might ask why she hadn't alerted my father to it but, to be fair, questioning my father's judgment just wasn't on the agenda and the man was one of his old and trusted friends.'

'Did you get on well with Kate?' asked Sarah.

'The last time I spoke to her, other than on the telephone, was at my father's funeral. You may have been told that I am a member of her club and I saw her flitting about there on a number of occasions, but she didn't like to get close to members and that certainly included me. You asked me if I got on well with her and the short answer is that I didn't and the feeling was entirely mutual. She looked upon me as a not very bright nonentity and I considered her to be a self-righteous poseuse. She was, though, I have to confess, a very bright cookie and ruthless with it.'

'What about the rest of her family?'

'There isn't one as far as I know. I gather that her mother died when she and her brother were very young and her father never married again. He was killed in a powerboat race a few years ago — bloody silly occupation, if you ask me. I suppose she might have had uncles, aunts and cousins, but she clearly wasn't one to talk about that sort of thing and frankly I just wasn't interested.'

'I gather that Kate Farrant's brother disappeared while serving with the SAS in Iraq,' said Sinclair.

'Yes. He is her twin brother, or perhaps I

should say was, and one of the most unpleasant people I have ever met. I am bound to admit that one of the reasons I so disliked him was that my father thought he was wonderful. I must say this for Adam, though, he knew how to handle the old man. He flattered him, listened to his tedious stories and fed him highly coloured tales about his time in Northern Ireland. I thought that Jane was immune to his charms, but I was wrong and I have cast-iron evidence for it. You see, just before Adam was posted to Iraq, my father, knowing that I was going to be abroad for a couple of weeks, asked me if I would lend him my flat for one of the weeks as he was coming to London for an intense briefing session and to get his injections and kit sorted out before he flew out there. I pointed out that it would have been proper and more courteous for him to have asked me directly himself and in any case why couldn't the War Office fix up somewhere for him to go? My father was not amused. He said that he himself would have been glad to accommodate him had he been in better health and he also gathered that security was involved and the authorities wanted his presence in London kept under wraps. I said that if they were that worried why didn't they fix him up with a safe house? At that my father flew off the handle. I received an earful about patriotism and the need to support those who had the courage and dedication to fight terrorism and dictatorship on our behalf. On top of that, he gave me a large dose of jingoistic claptrap, which was pretty rich coming from him. After all, where had all his money come from? I'll tell you, it was from the distinctly shady property deals that he and my grandfather indulged in just after the war. They seem to have been a lot more subtle about it than people like Rackman but, reading between the lines, they were very much tarred with the same brush.

'He also gave me a lot of flannel about influential people he knew who had hinted that if it became known that Adam was being briefed about undercover work in Iraq, he would be in grave danger. If you ask me, my father had been reading too much about T E Lawrence and was taken in by Adam's hints that he might have to pose as an Arab in order to infiltrate Al-Qaeda. There was also his service in Northern Ireland, which my father thought was wonderful, as he believed that Adam was working clandestinely there as well.

'It seemed to me much more likely that Adam wanted to use the flat as a knocking shop and I was right. He was either stupid enough to believe that he had covered his tracks, or much more likely, didn't care tuppence if I found out. The fact is that he had just heaved the sheets he used into the dirty clothes basket and there were certain stains on them. I am not exactly proud of the fact that I tested them with an acid phosphatase kit and the powder duly turned dark purple.'

'Did you have an idea who his partner was?' Sinclair asked.

'I both had an idea and was able to confirm it. I also found some hairs on the sheets and a detective agency I consulted was able to match them with some samples from Jane's comb, which she conveniently left behind on her desk when she was taken ill, after that episode with Adam.'

'On the face of it, that seems a strange and extreme thing to have done,' said Sarah, puzzled.

'It was amour-propre, I suppose. I wasn't going to be taken as a complete nonentity by either of them.'

'Did you already have some suspicions about Jane Fisher, then?'

'Not with regard to the charity's finances, but I did wonder if Adam had had a finger in that particular pie and was using Jane for his own purposes. Pure idle speculation, of course, but I did discover from his father's will, which I looked up, that he had been left out of it completely.'

'Any idea why?'

'I did wonder if he had blotted his copybook in some way or other in the past, but I had neither the inclination nor the energy to pursue it any further. All I can say is that I am glad to be shot of the charity and all those associated with it.'

'Did you find Jane attractive yourself?'

The man smiled. 'I am not exactly a qualified judge of female pulchritude as I am immune to Cupid's darts.' He gave a little bow in Sarah's direction. 'Let there be no misunderstanding. I'm no misogynist, nor am I a homosexual. Asexual might be the most appropriate description. Of course I have been extremely upset about all that has happened in the last year or so, not least when Miss Corsie rang to tell me about Kate's death, and you mustn't think that my flippant attitude means that I wasn't. Psychiatrists would no doubt say that I use it to hide my many insecurities and maybe they would be right.'

'Did you go to the club the evening that Kate was taken ill?'

'Yes, Miss Corsie was good enough to mention that fact to me when she notified me of Kate's death. I was busy during the following week and had no idea that she had been ill that night, let alone mortally so. The news came as a complete shock.'

'Did you see Kate that night?'

'I just caught sight of her on a couple of occasions. As I've already told you, we weren't exactly on chatting terms. I'm not saying that she would have turned her back on me if we had come face to face with other people around, but tactical avoidance was the usual scenario.'

'Do you remember if she was her usual self that night? Physically, I mean,' asked Sarah.

'My views of her were so brief that I couldn't possibly say. I seem to remember that she was walking about quite briskly and I certainly didn't notice that there was anything wrong or unusual about her.'

'If, as you have just told me, you resented Kate Farrant in many ways, why is it that you belonged to the club and visited it quite often?'

'Because it amuses me. No, I am not a serious gambler, but I like watching others at it. Their triumphs, their disasters and despairs produce a feeling of electricity that is difficult to describe, but is one which I enjoy. I also have to admit that it gave me a certain adolescent type of pleasure knowing that my presence made Kate feel uncomfortable. She tried not to show it, of course, and as I told you she didn't often appear in the gambling rooms, but I sensed that she wondered what I was up to and there were not enough subtleties in that rigid personality of hers to realize that it was the one way I had of getting under her skin. Pretty petty, that, wasn't it?'

'Did Kate get on well with her brother?'

'They hated each other. They were always getting at each other as children, being intense rivals. Adam used his superior strength and Kate her brains. She knew exactly how to wind him up and took care to do it when their father or grandfather were in the vicinity. Richard Farrant must surely have been aware of it and I can't imagine why he decided to send them to the same boarding school, Brantley College. Someone told me that they weren't on speaking terms latterly and it's quite possible that he had that affair with Jane Fisher, knowing that Kate was quite likely to find out, just to stir her up. He really was a vile man.'

'Have you any plans to travel to Hungary, or anywhere else abroad, in the near future?'

'No. Have you any particular reason for asking?'

'Just that our enquiries are likely to go on

for some time and we may need to see you again.'

The man raised his eyebrows slightly. 'Never fear, I enjoyed our little chat. It was a welcome diversion as I have got rather bogged down in the tedious task of translating some distinctly opaque technical instructions on how to operate some electronic pieces of apparatus manufactured in Hungary. I am not going anywhere for the foreseeable future and look forward to meeting you again should the need arise.'

3

Back in the car on their way back to the Yard, Sinclair looked across at Sarah, who was driving. 'What did you make of him?' he asked.

'He clearly likes to play the buffoon, but he's no fool and on the whole I thought his view of what went on at the charity was more likely to be reliable than that of Margaret Nanson. I did, though, find his comments about Kate Farrant difficult to read. She very obviously queered his pitch over the management of the charity and yet he appears not to have felt any ill will against her over that. I even got the impression from the way he talked about her that he almost admired her in some respects.'

'Yes and he made no bones about his hatred of Adam Farrant, who sounds like a very nasty piece of work indeed from all that we have discovered about him. I think the whole of that family needs to be looked into as far as possible, so why don't we see what we can dig up in the records as a start?'

'Good idea. How do you get on with Reg

Barnes, though? He frightens the life out of me.'

'He's all right if you just ignore his gruff exterior,' Sinclair said.

Despite her reservations, Sarah had to admit that, at least on this occasion, despite being as dour and unsmiling as ever, the man was remarkably helpful.

'We're working on the case of the young woman, Kate Farrant, who was poisoned and died a few days later,' Sinclair said. 'You've no doubt heard about it and I wondered if you had anything on her or her father Richard and brother Adam.'

Sinclair was half expecting the man to ask him why he hadn't looked it up himself, but to his relief he just grunted and brought up the details on the screen. There was more on Farrant senior, than he had expected, with details of his powerboat and motor-racing experience. He had been killed in 2005 during a race on the water in Florida and there was a short video of the accident. The vessel with its crew of two was in the lead when it appeared to hit something, the bow shot up in the air and the boat cleared the water completely, landing upside-down. At that time the man had been fifty-one and had been competing for many years with moderate success, having achieved a number of wins. He had also taken part in hill climbs and various races for vintage cars, was a qualified pilot and also ran a gambling club in London. He had married in 1977 and the twins were born the following year, his wife taking her own life soon afterwards. There were several colour photographs of the man sitting in his boat, standing by a Cessna light aircraft and a close-up of him in a white tracksuit, holding a helmet. They had already seen from his portrait in the club that he was extremely good-looking, with thick black hair, and was powerfully built. A section on memories of him were almost exclusively about his racing career on sea and land, although a number of women had e-mailed with reminiscences of his charm and attraction. There was also a mention of his son Adam having gone missing believed killed in Iraq and of Kate being in the chair of The Frampton Trust and owner of The Spinning Wheel Club.

There was nothing on Sir Henry Frampton apart from his obituary, which went to town on his charitable activities and his Foundation, and finally Sinclair asked Barnes if he'd look up the QC Rupert Chester and raised his eyebrows when he saw the entry, pointing it out to Sarah.

'It looks to me as if this is something Tyrrell will need to tackle.'

She nodded. 'I agree.'

★ ★ ★

'The other person who interests me, both from what you found out from Miss Nanson and from what Paul Frampton told us,' Sinclair said, when they were back in Sarah's flat, 'is Adam Farrant. I think it would be a good idea to see what we can dig up on him. Why don't I give my uncle a ring? He was in the army, like my father, and being a widower, without children, spends a lot of time doing voluntary work at the Imperial War Museum. He's bound to have access to all sorts of military records. I'm in need of a tutorial on the SAS and he might well have heard something on the grapevine about the man's disappearance. If he doesn't know about the SAS himself, he most certainly will have contacts who do.'

★ ★ ★

The two of them met Brigadier Sinclair at the museum the following morning. He must, Sarah thought, have been in his seventies, but he looked and sounded much younger, with

80

his alert demeanour, clipped speech and quick movements.

'Heard about you from my sister-in-law,' he said, when Mark had introduced her to him. 'Don't worry, she approves. Enjoy sleuthing, do you?'

'Very much. The head of our section's an excellent man. He's always there for advice, but lets us use our initiative.'

The man nodded. 'As it should be, but isn't always. I know about that. Well, young Mark, what's all this about?'

Sinclair gave him a brief resume of the case. 'So you see, we are trying to find out as much as possible about this man Adam Farrant. Not only was he the brother of the woman whose death we are investigating and who ran a charity to help victims of Alzheimer's disease, but also knew the son of the founder of the charity. Apart from that, he appears to have been having an affair with the woman who, it is alleged, had been plundering the funds by fiddling cheques. More intriguing still is the fact that he was in the SAS and disappeared in Iraq while supposedly being involved in undercover work. It has been assumed that he was killed by insurgents, but inevitably we have been wondering if he absconded and made his way back to England. His twin sister was running

81

the charity and you may have read about their father. He was a well-known adventurer and sportsman who was killed during a powerboat race in the States some years ago when he was in his early fifties. The accident was filmed and I saw a recording of the video of it yesterday. I gather it was also shown on TV at the time.'

The brigadier nodded and looked at him quizzically. 'And do I take it that you want to pick my brains about the SAS?'

'Exactly that.'

'Hmm. Well, yes, I do know a little about it. Are you familiar with the SAS, my dear?' Sarah shook her head. 'It's a full-time regiment, selected from volunteers from various branches of the British army. It was founded by David Stirling during the African campaign of the Second World War and operates in small, mobile fighting columns. It is unusual in that only the NCOs and privates are permanent members and they even have a say in the selection of the officers, whom they refer to as 'Ruperts' and who only serve for two to three years before returning to their units. Apart from actions in the Falklands and more recently in Afghanistan and Iraq, the regiment has operated on 'special' missions and there has been a move to restrict their activities to that field of operations. You no doubt remember that Norman Kember and two Canadian colleagues were rescued by them in 2006 and perhaps the man you are interested in was involved in that. I had heard that one of their officers had disappeared some time later and maybe he's your man. I'll do my best to find out a bit more about it for you, but it may prove difficult. Give me a day or two and I'll get back to you.'

★ ★ ★

The call from Mark Sinclair's uncle came the following afternoon and he agreed to come round to Sarah's flat for supper that evening.

'Thanks for the warning about obsessive punctuality,' Sarah said, giving Mark a grin as, at precisely the time they had arranged, there was a ring on the doorbell.

'Nice place you've got here,' the man said, when Mark had shown him round and Sarah came in from the kitchen and joined them in the sitting room.

'I had the good fortune to inherit it,' Sarah said, 'and I shudder to think where I might have landed had that not been the case.'

The man nodded. 'If the Met Police provide accommodation at all, it couldn't be worse than the awful places my wife had to put up with in the army for years after we married.'

He kept them entertained with tales of some of his postings and adventures when he was on active service until, after they had eaten and over coffee, he opened his briefcase and took out some sheets of paper.

'My task on this fellow didn't prove too difficult, that's why I have been quicker than I anticipated. What made it easy is that there was an enquiry after his disappearance in Iraq and I managed to get a sight of the report — they wouldn't let me have a copy of it — and I also have some further information about him. Perhaps it would be best if I put it in chronological order. He was born in 1978, one of non-identical twins, a boy and a girl, whose parents were Richard and Elizabeth Farrant. His mother died within a short time of their birth and you already know about the father, who was killed in that powerboat accident when he was in his fifties. Both the children were educated at Brantley College in Berkshire and he went on to Sandhurst, where he won the Queen's Medal. He applied to join the SAS while serving with his regiment in Northern Ireland, passed the selection procedure and was sent to Iraq in 2006 and that is where it all gets rather blurred.

'You see, an enquiry into the beating and torture of some Iraqi prisoners, in which he was implicated, was in the process of being set up and it was at about that time that he disappeared. Earlier on he had taken a course in Arabic — evidently he had a talent for languages — and it was rumoured that he was in the habit of dressing up as a native and that he was trying to infiltrate some of the terrorist elements. That all happened a good two years ago, nothing has been heard of him since and none of the various factions with a record of abductions in the past have claimed responsibility.'

'And what is the view of the military authorities?' Sinclair asked.

'Inevitably, with the possibility of a court martial — one of the other ranks had pointed the finger at him for being responsible for sanctioning torture of prisoners and civilians and indeed taking part in that himself — it was considered that he might have gone AWOL. However, as absolutely nothing has been heard or even rumoured about him since, it is considered most likely that he was killed by one of the dissident groups and buried somewhere. I imagine it's quite on the cards that one of his victims survived and tipped the wink to dissidents, who might well have been only too pleased to eliminate him.'

'Did you get a sight of any confidential reports about his previous service either in Iraq or Northern Ireland?'

'Nothing that I was allowed to see, but one of the people I spoke to, who served with him in Northern Ireland, said that he was very bright and physically tough, but prone to take risks, some of which were both unnecessary and even foolhardy. I've come across a few like that myself, many of them who'd been in Burma during the last war and others later on in Korea. Men like that are completely lost during periods of inaction or during home postings. One way of coping with them has been to use them as instructors in the selection and training of organizations such as the SAS and the Marine Commandos.'

'Am I right in thinking that there have been several instances of ex-SAS men getting into trouble when back in civilian life, both other ranks and officers?'

'I've heard so, but I don't have chapter and verse.'

'And what about the possibility of a man like Farrant being able to find his was back to the UK, if he had absconded?' asked Sarah.

'If desperate, ill-educated people who don't even speak the language are able to do so literally in their thousands, I don't see why not. Do you seriously consider that he might be implicated in the death of his sister which you are investigating?'

'It's a possibility we have to consider, but I have to admit that it's a pretty long shot. The two of them appear to have been at daggers drawn for many years and we do know that he was having a sexual relationship with a woman who might have been rather too free with the petty cash belonging to the charity for which she was working and that his sister was running. It was happening just before he went to Iraq. Is there any chance, do you think, of being able to speak to someone who knew him well in the army?'

'I'm pretty sure that no one in the SAS would be prepared to talk, but there might perhaps be someone who was with him at Sandhurst and kept up with him. I'll see what I can do about that. Intriguing stuff you have to deal with. Be sure to let me know how it turns out.'

★ ★ ★

The two detectives met Roger Tyrrell in his office the following morning.

'Has Jack found anything of interest in that flat?' he asked.

'He hasn't finished down there yet and I will be given a conducted tour when he has.

However, he did tell me that the administrator, Jill Corsie, got hold of a firm of contract cleaners later in the morning after Miss Farrant was admitted to hospital. That was only reasonable as the poor woman had soiled her bed and the floor between the bathroom and the bedroom before the ambulance had had time to get to her, at which time she was only semi-conscious. Miss Corsie wasn't to know that there was anything suspicious about the illness and could hardly have been expected to delay getting it cleaned up, fearing that if it had been left the smell would have spread to the rest of the house. The carpet in the bedroom was pulled up and taken away and Jack discovered that it had been incinerated.

'I gather that the flat is quite large and in addition to the living quarters, Miss Farrant had a large office, in which were details of the club's finances, lists of members and employees and a separate filing cabinet for her own personal and financial affairs. Some of the documents are still being studied, but a preliminary study of them and interviews with her bank manager and her club's solicitor suggest that not only was Miss Farrant an extremely wealthy woman but the club was also prospering and all its affairs were in good order. There is still a good deal to do, but evidently there was a remarkable lack of personal effects, such as family photographs and correspondence down there, and no evidence has been found so far that she had made a will. If she did, it is not in the flat, nor is there a copy lodged with the solicitor who deals with the affairs of the club. I suppose it's possible that she had a property elsewhere and employed a different firm for her private affairs.'

'Any evidence for that?'

'Not that has been discovered so far.'

'Did she own a car?'

'Yes, a practically new Porsche Boxter was in the garage at the side of the house and there is a record of its purchase a few months ago — Jack will be able to tell you the details about it.'

'Well, it's early days yet and something else may well turn up. Did you find out anything else about her?'

'We've interviewed a number of people,' Sinclair replied, 'and found out some quite interesting things about her and the charity.' He went on to describe what Miss Corsie, Miss Nanson and Paul Frampton had said. 'It seems quite clear that the Farrant twins, Kate and Adam, hated each other's guts and I think that would be well worth pursuing. My uncle is doing what he can over Adam's service in the SAS and we were wondering if it would be worth enquiring at Brantley College where the twins attended for five years.'

'Just a moment,' Tyrrell said. 'I used to play regularly in the Halford Hewitt Cup at Sandwich until this job destroyed what was left of my golf and my partner and I played against a fellow, one David Barclay, whom I'm pretty sure became headmaster of Brantley College. That was all of ten years ago, but he might still be there. At any rate, it's worth taking a look on the website.'

'Did you and your partner win, sir?' Sarah asked, grinning.

Tyrrell smiled. 'Fortunately not and he's bound to remember the result and that might make him more disposed to help us.'

He quickly brought up the college on the internet and found both the phone number and that the man was still headmaster.

'Sorry to bother you when I know you must be busy at this time of day,' he said when he got through. 'This is Roger Tyrrell. You may remember that you and your partner saw us off at Sandwich a few years back — in '98, I think it was.'

The man gave a chuckle. 'Hardly saw you off! It was at the twentieth, wasn't it? Still detecting, are you?'

'Yes and the reason I'm ringing is that we need some background on the Farrant twins. You almost certainly will have heard that Kate died very recently in distinctly unusual circumstances and Adam went missing in Iraq about eighteen months ago. Ring any bells?'

'It certainly does and some rather disquieting ones. I'd rather not say anything more over the phone. Any chance of your coming down here for a chat?'

'I'm afraid that I'm tied up with a different enquiry for the next week or two. My two assistants Inspector Sarah Prescott and Inspector Mark Sinclair are leading the enquiry.'

'I take it from their names that one of them is a woman,' said Barclay.

'Does that bother you?' asked Tyrell, surprised.

'No, the very reverse, the reasons for which will become clear when I see them. It so happens that I can make myself available mid-afternoon today. Would that suit?'

'Hang on a moment. I'll ask them.'

When the arrangement had been finalized and Tyrrell had replaced the receiver, he looked at his assistants across the desk. 'I won't give you a name at the moment, but just let me say that a certain senior member of the force is nagging me a bit over this case.

He wants some action and it's no great surprise that he happens to be a member of The Spinning Wheel Club. Enough said, but perhaps you'd let me know how you get on. Give me a call at home this evening, say about ten o'clock.'

'There is one other thing, sir, that we both think is a bit too sensitive for us,' said Sinclair. 'You see, one of the members of the club appears to have been having an affair with one of the croupiers and Miss Farrant dismissed the girl and the man had his membership withdrawn.'

'And?'

'We looked the man concerned, one Rupert Chester, up on the internet. He's a QC and his speciality is divorce — he's been involved in quite a few high-profile cases, involving titled people and pop stars and million-pound settlements.'

'Has he, now? That's interesting,' said Tyrell. 'Does his entry say anything about his marriage?'

'Yes, he's married to a peer's younger daughter and they have two young children.'

'Well, that certainly bears being looked into. I'll make a few enquiries myself while you two are busy at Brantley College.'

★ ★ ★

Roger Tyrrell sat at his desk for a good ten minutes after Sinclair and Prescott left, deep in thought. Then he pressed the buzzer next to the telephone.

'Would you get a phone number for me, please, Jane?'

'Of course, sir.'

'You should be able to get that and the man's home address from Jack Pocock. He was a member of The Spinning Wheel Club and had his membership withdrawn some months before Miss Farrant's death. Despite that, I think it likely that Miss Farrant kept a record of his particulars. I am particularly anxious that there should be no hint that I am making enquiries about him and perhaps you'd pass that on to Jack as well. The man in question is one Rupert Chester and he is a QC, specializing in divorce cases. It is his home number that I'm after as well as his address and I'd also be interested in any personal details you are able to pick up. I have to go to a meeting now, but should be back here by five and . . . No, on second thoughts these wretched meetings have a habit of dragging on. Perhaps first thing tomorrow morning would be better.'

'I could always telephone you at home, sir, if you'd prefer it,' said Jane.

'No, thank you. It can wait until tomorrow,' decided Tyrell.

★   ★   ★

On Sunday morning Tyrrell drove out to the address he had been given. The house was in a gated estate roughly halfway between Wimbledon and Kingston. Like the others in the area, it was a substantial property with a large garden. He parked out of sight of the house on the private road and made his way up the drive on foot, and almost at once heard the sound of a motor mower and saw the back view of a man sitting on it as he was starting another run across the extensive lawn away from him. The detective waited beside a large oak tree until the man came into view again and then stepped forward.

The man looked startled at the sight of him, pulled up and then got off the seat and walked towards him. He was just about to say something when Tyrrell held up his hand, showing his warrant card.

'Mr Chester?'

'Yes.'

'Chief Superintendent Tyrrell, Metropolitan Police. May I have a word? In private.'

'It's not at all convenient just now. You see, my wife . . . '

'There's no need for her to be involved. It's about Kate Farrant. Why don't we go over to the garden seat over there.'

The man, who looked to be in his late forties, had gone pale. He stood for a moment without saying anything and then nodded.

'Very well.'

When they were sitting side by side, the man turned and look very directly at the detective. 'Now,' he said, 'perhaps you'd tell me what this is all about?'

'As you probably know, a few weeks ago Kate Farrant was admitted to St Gregory's Hospital with severe gastroenteritis and she died three days later. I don't need to tell you that she was the owner of The Spinning Wheel Club of which you were a member until some months ago when you were told by her that your membership had been withdrawn with immediate effect. She didn't die from natural causes, Mr Chester, she was poisoned some time during the afternoon of 11 June while at the club. Would you mind telling me what you were doing on that afternoon?'

'May I ask why you want to know that?'

'I'm quite sure you know exactly why, but I'll spell it out for you. The reason why your membership was terminated was because you were having a relationship with one of the croupiers — the two of you were picked up by the security cameras having a distinctly intimate and enthusiastic embrace as you left the club and the young woman, when confronted by Miss Farrant, told her what the two of you had been doing and didn't even try to justify herself or make excuses. In my experience, a lot of girls in that situation would have tried to put the entire blame on the man, but she didn't and, reading between the lines, made it clear that as far as she was concerned, she was well shot of the place.

'Under the circumstances, I'm quite sure that someone like you, who is well versed in this sort of scenario in your work, will understand why I am here. Would you care to tell me about it? If you do so and I am satisfied that you had nothing to do with Miss Farrant's death, or indeed anything illegal, then that will be the end of it.'

'If I don't, what then?'

'I have no intention of threatening you. But you must be only too well aware that if this gets out, the consequences for your family and professional life might be compromised.'

The man glanced back in the direction of the house. 'The things that worry me most about all this, as you appear to have appreciated, is my wife and family. For that reason, I think we'd better go up to the house and say that a new piece of information has suddenly come to light concerning a case in which I am involved and needs to be sorted out before the court reconvenes tomorrow. I'll do the explaining.'

Diana Chester was painfully thin and looked anxiously at the detective after he had been introduced as plain Roger Tyrrell and her husband had outlined the situation.

'I'm so sorry to have had to disturb your Sunday like this,' Tyrrell said, smiling at her. 'I'll be as quick as I can.'

'Won't you stay for lunch?'

'That would be asking too much and, in any case, I have to get back to London. Thank you for asking me.'

The two men went into the study and Chester looked at the detective without lowering his eyes across the desk.

'Two years ago, my wife got pregnant for the second time — we also have a five-year-old girl. Although it was planned, I did have reservations about it as Diana got quite badly depressed after the birth of our daughter and I was warned that there might well be a recurrence with another pregnancy. Diana became almost hysterical when I expressed my reservations and accused me of not wanting the son on whom she had set her heart. Her parents didn't help, either, encouraging her despite the warnings of our GP. Things went wrong right from the start. Diana had serious trouble with sickness during the pregnancy and became so depressed that a termination was even considered, though by then it was too late anyway. If anything, the situation got even worse after the baby was born. She didn't want anything to do with the tiny boy. Breastfeeding was out of the question but despite being premature and weighing under five pounds at birth, he picked up quickly and was an easy baby. I had to employ a full-time resident nanny. My in-laws were worse than useless — maybe they even felt some guilt at having pressed Diana to go ahead with the second pregnancy and there was the under-current feeling, of which I was only too well aware, that I was not worthy of their daughter and that she had married beneath her. As for my parents, they are divorced and my mother never did get on with Diana. Her health has slowly improved, but as you've seen for yourself, she remains vulnerable, underweight and desperately anxious, although at least she is less depressed and we've still got the nanny. As for our sex life, it doesn't exist and hasn't done so ever since she became pregnant and I have serious doubts that it ever will.

'When I was staying overnight in my flat at the chambers, I quite often went to The Spinning Wheel in the evenings, just to get away from my thoughts and misery. I liked the people there, the atmosphere was relaxed and I enjoyed a gentle flutter. I always knew when to stop and just about broke even during the time I played there. It was about six months ago when I was at the roulette table that I happened to glance up and saw Cathy looking at me. I still have a picture of it in my mind; as our eyes met, the tip of her tongue appeared just beyond her lips.

'There wasn't anything that young woman wouldn't let me do to her, nor her to me, and, believe me, she enjoyed it all every bit as much as I did. I got careless that evening; I was so looking forward to what we had planned that I clean forgot about the security camera by the side door. My time with her was the best I ever had in that way, but that final night was also the finish of it all.

'I'm not blaming Kate Farrant at all. There were clear rules, which was one of the reasons why the club was so free from scandal, and I had broken them. I also have to say that she didn't make a meal out of it when she confronted me, nor did she threaten me with disclosure, or anything like that, and I didn't try to pretend outraged innocence. She also told me that she had briefed the security officer, who was an ex policeman and, as far as she and the club were concerned, apart from my membership being withdrawn, the matter was closed. I like to think that we parted with some degree of mutual respect and that was certainly true from my point of view.

'As for Cathy, she wasn't bothered in the least about losing her job — she told me that had it not been for me, she would have left earlier, being fed up with the petty regulations governing the girls at the club. As for our relationship, there wasn't one, merely an arrangement that provided good sex and excitement that suited us both at the time, but had no long-term future. If you like, Cathy had a very male outlook to matters like that and we parted with no hard feelings.

'I wasn't worried for myself, either, when I heard about Kate Farrant's death. Of course I was sorry about it, but I hadn't liked her — I thought she was totally lacking in charm and appeared to be a humourless robot. I also had no reason to believe that her death was anything more than due to natural causes, but now, of course, you've come on to the scene and told me she was poisoned. How was it that you discovered about my indiscretion, if one can put it that way?'

'We found a record of the incident in Kate Farrant's papers at the club,' Tyrell told him. 'Now, we know that Kate Farrant was taken ill on 11 June. Would you mind telling me what you were doing during that day and also in the evening?'

'That's easy. It was young Sophie's birthday and I was in court that day. Luckily it was only for the morning and I was able to get back here early that afternoon and help with the preparations for the birthday party. In many ways that event was a bit of a breakthrough, as Diana not only saw it through with my help and that of the nanny, but even managed to enjoy it. I'm quite sure that one or the other would be able to confirm that if it's absolutely necessary.'

'I think that would be worthwhile,' said Tyrell.

'All right.'

When they went back into the kitchen and joined Diana, Chester seemed about to say something, but the detective forestalled him.

'I'd just like to apologize again for disturbing your Sunday morning, but perhaps your husband didn't mind too much; I know to my cost that lawnmowing is something of a tedious bore when all one wants to do at the weekend is relax with the family. Your husband was telling me about Sophie's party.'

The detective turned towards the small girl, who was sitting at the table working on a ball of pastry that she had just started to roll out. 'Making biscuits, are you?' She nodded and gave him a smile. 'Your daddy was telling me about your party. Was it fun?'

'Yes. There was a conjurer and he had a real rabbit, which came out of his hat, and he took an egg out of Daddy's ear.'

'My goodness, I never had anything like that when I was your age. How old are you?'

'Five.'

'It must be nice having a birthday in June. Mine is in December and very near to Christmas, so sometimes I only got one lot of presents. That isn't very fair, is it?' The little girl shook her head. 'Do you know what day of the month your birthday is?'

The small child gave him a withering look. 'Course I do. The eleventh.'

'That was a silly question, wasn't it? I hope the biscuits are a success. Goodbye, everyone.'

4

David Barclay was a sandy-haired, trim-looking man, who, Sarah thought, looked to be in his early fifties.

'I thought I would get hold of the college register for you,' he said, when he and the two detectives had introduced themselves to each other and were sitting in his study over a cup of tea. 'It always helps to get dates right and so I dug it out after Tyrrell had spoken to me. I gather that you are enquiring about Adam Farrant.'

'Yes, you no doubt saw and heard the reports in the media that he went missing in Iraq and the possibilities of his either having been kidnapped or murdered were raised,' said Sarah.

'Yes and not only that; one of his contemporaries here, who also went to Sandhurst and who came to the last Founder's Day celebrations, told me that there had been problems over his time out there.'

'What sort of problems?' asked Sinclair.

'You must have heard that some of our men were found guilty of beating and abusing

103

prisoners and civilians out there and although nothing was proved about Adam's involvement, there were rumours.'

'Did you know him well yourself when he was here?' Sinclair asked.

'Indeed I did, but I'd better refresh my memory. Let's see.' He flicked through the pages of the register. 'Yes, here we are. I had only been head here for four years or so when he and his twin sister came to the college. Their father, Richard, was an old boy and as it happened I knew him well because we were both at Durham University together. It was obvious right from the start that Adam was going to be a formidable games player and in due course he became one of our best rugby players and an even better cricketer. As to his sister, Kate, she was quite simply the brightest pupil we have had in my time here.'

'Did you teach either of them?'

'Unfortunately I am too busy to teach all that often, but from time to time I do my stuff in modern languages if one of the staff in that department is ill, but if I did have either of them in my classes, it made no impression on me. However, I did get to know them both quite well when they became college prefects. Kate was appointed and indeed became head of the college purely on merit, but Adam was only a college prefect by virtue of being captain of cricket. That particular combination was part of a longstanding tradition, but has since been abandoned and not before time, in my opinion. You see, Adam's position here at that time was pivotal in a very serious matter, which had it not been effectively hushed up, would probably have resulted in my having to resign. It was a complicated business, but I'll do my best to make it clear and I think it would be best if I explained first how my friendship with Richard Farrant developed.'

* * *

David Barclay came from a modest background; his father ran a hardware store, and he himself went to the local comprehensive school. Not only did he prove bright, but after he had obtained a holiday job helping out at the pro's shop at the local golf club, what followed changed his life for ever. He was allowed to have a hit late in the afternoons on the practice ground and one of the members, a low handicap player, spotted at once that he had a real natural talent for the game. Of course it hadn't happened at once, but he had then taken proper lessons and as a result of that, and the fact that he was personable, clever and hard working, he was offered an assisted place at a public school where golf had been a tradition for many years.

The two years at that school made his first term at Durham a great deal easier than it might have been had he gone straight there from a state comprehensive. By that time he had become used to living away from home and like others in that situation before him, he had one accent for home and the other for school. In his first term at university he had a room in one of the student hostels, but it was not long before he joined Richard Farrant and two others in a rented house. He would not have even considered it had not Richard, who in that first term had a room along the corridor, made the suggestion. In fact, it wasn't a suggestion: the man, who was two years older than almost all the other first-year students, having done two years' work experience with a firm that made racing car and powerboat engines, was an almost irresistible force. He was charming, a brilliant cricket and hockey player and a human dynamo. It wasn't fair, David thought; he was even exceptionally good-looking.

It was hardly surprising that the girls should have flocked around him, but he wasn't interested in them, only having eyes for Annabel Frith, with whom he started to go out in their second year. It seemed an unlikely match; she had a scholarship, was reading physics and was as intense, serious and seemingly dedicated to her academic work as Richard was outgoing and cheerful and equally dedicated to sport. There was no doubting that she was very clever, much more so than him, and she could have been nice-looking, even pretty, had she not been so thin and seemingly uninterested in making the best of herself. There was another side to her, though, and at times it was almost as if someone had pressed a switch inside her, switching on all the lights. David remembered, in particular, the ball held just before they left the university. Annabel was all over Richard throughout the evening but when David asked her to dance, she pressed herself against him, moving from side to side with sinuous gyrations and gently nipping his ear with her teeth. David was convinced that Richard must have seen what was happening to him because he suddenly appeared, swept Annabel into his arms and they whirled away, while David just managed to hide his own only too obvious arousal and slipped out of the room on to the terrace outside, pacing around until he had got control of himself.

A year after they had gone down from

Durham and David was at Exeter doing his PGCE, he was invited to Richard and Annabel's wedding. It was a very grand affair and was held at the country house near Beaconsfield in Buckinghamshire owned by Richard's father. Annabel's family was only represented by her mother, who seemed both out of place and uncomfortable, and one of David's more waspish female acquaintances from his time at Durham was only too happy to say how embarrassing the poor woman must be finding it, being a single mother with no one there to support her. David was so sickened by the remark that he went up to the woman, who was standing on her own, and explained that he had known Annabel at university and wasn't she looking lovely? The gesture wasn't a success and when he got little response, gave up after a few minutes, excusing himself by saying that he must have a word with Richard's father.

He was often to wonder over the next few years how the marriage had worked out, but with the rapid advance of his career, his own marriage and then the headship of Brantley College, he had other things to think about. It was a strange coincidence that he should have finished up as headmaster of the school where Richard had had such a meteoric career as a schoolboy. Had that been one of the reasons why he had applied for the job? Maybe, he thought, that notion wasn't so fanciful as all that. There had undoubtedly been a touch of hero worship about his friendship with Farrant and it wasn't entirely a surprise when he discovered that Richard's twins had been put down on the waiting list of the college soon after they were born.

It was when Kate had been entered for a scholarship that Richard got in touch with David and said that he would like to bring her to the college for the exam and that it would also be a good opportunity for him to show her and his son round. During their visit the two men had a long chat on their own.

'There are some things, David, that you should know about the twins, although I would like what I have to tell you to remain strictly between the two of us. I have thought long and hard about this, but I think it is in their interests that you should be aware of the background. I don't know how much you know already.'

'Very little apart from the terrible news about Annabel and that she had had twins. You probably remember that I wrote to you at the time.'

Farrant nodded. 'Yes and it was very much appreciated.'

There was a very long pause and then the man began.

* * *

Richard Farrant had had several girlfriends after leaving school and in his first year at Durham. It had all been so easy for him. He had been a target for the extrovert, hard-drinking set of young women, many of whom were on the lookout for casual sex with a good-looking, personable and extremely talented games player. It had been fun and neither he nor they looked for anything more to it than that. Annabel was someone quite different. She was serious-minded, very clever and restrained in her behaviour, neither drinking nor taking the drugs that were so easy to obtain and making it clear that full sex was only for after marriage.

After the wedding had taken place and they had taken up residence in the cottage in the grounds of the Farrant country house while looking for a place of their own, it wasn't as if someone had pressed a switch, it was more as if there was a spring inside her that was being slowly wound up. Having always thought carefully about what she was going to say, she began to make direct and embarrassing remarks to people, to laugh frequently and sometimes immoderately, and from being shy and reticent became almost exhibitionist. On holiday the following year, by one of the Italian lakes, she began to demand forms of sex that he had never even broached with her, even delighting in appearing naked in front of him, something she had previously been so shy about that she avoided it whenever possible. That had culminated in the profoundly embarrassing scene that had occurred when they were sitting by the hotel pool one morning. They had been having a cup of coffee at a table under a sunshade, when she suddenly said:

'God, I'm hot. Let's go in for a swim.'

'Good idea,' he replied. 'I'll just nip up to our room and get our costumes.'

She gave a laugh and said, 'I'm not going to wait that long.'

There and then she stripped off all her clothes and dived into the pool.

Somehow, Farrant managed to deal with the situation without their being asked to leave. He snatched up one of the hotel towels from a nearby lounger, dived in himself, wrapped her in it and carried her back to their room. That was the start of it; during the rest of their holiday she was insatiable, wanting to do all the things she had refused before. He managed to calm her down by slipping the antihistamines he had brought for his hayfever into her drinks and somehow they got through the rest of the holiday without having to return early.

She did agree to see her GP, but by that time she was much more like her old self and the woman made reassuring noises to her, saying that it was probably no more than the excitement of the holiday. Farrant knew it was more serious than that and he was quite sure that she must have hidden a lot of what had happened, but she absolutely refused to allow him to talk to the GP nor would she contemplate a visit to a psychiatrist. That suggestion had provoked a furious response.

'Do you think I'm mad or something?' she had shouted at him.

He managed to calm her down and gradually she seemed to get back to her previous self, even starting work at a physics laboratory.

Annabel's greatest and frequently expressed wish at that time was to have a baby and Farrant decided that he really needed to find out more about her condition, even if it had to be in the abstract. He had already taken an interest in his father's gambling club and it was through that that he met a psychiatrist who agreed to have a general chat to him.

'You say that she refuses to see someone like me and that her GP has been dealing with the problem?' the man said when Farrant described the change in her, culminating in the episode in Italy.

'Yes. It is perfectly true that she has calmed down a lot and indeed I'd say she was pretty well back to her old self, but now she is very keen on having a baby and when I approached her GP with a view to asking her opinion, the woman said she was very sorry, but Annabel had told her quite specifically that she wasn't to speak to me or anyone else about her health. Dr Melville was as tactful as she could have been and said she understood my anxiety about her, but she was bound to respect her patient's wishes, not least because she was satisfied that she had recovered completely. I like the woman, although I am not a patient of hers, and I don't think she would have told Annabel that I had approached her. To be fair, I have no doubt I would have been upset and angry if Annabel had done the same to me, but I am still so concerned about her that I decided to ask an expert for their opinion. I would quite understand if you preferred not to comment, but I hope you understand my anxieties.'

The man had nodded. 'I assure you that I do, but it is very difficult to say much under these circumstances. Just let me say that it sounds as if she had an episode of what we call hypomania, which is often, but not always, associated with attacks of depression. This condition may run in families, but does not always do so and I gather you don't know a great deal about her family history anyway. The future is impossible to predict after just one episode, particularly without being able to go into your wife's past and family history in great detail. You are obviously worried about the effects of a pregnancy and once again I'm not able to help you other than with generalizations. Here I am, though, and if she changes her mind about a consultation, I would be only too pleased to help to the best of my ability.'

Farrant was still keen to wait until Annabel had had a long period of stability before she embarked on a pregnancy, or for that matter house hunting for a place of their own, and he thought that she was in tune with the idea. He also put on hold his ambition to take up powerboat racing and concentrated his efforts on getting to grips with the gambling club in South Kensington that his father was keen for him to take over.

For the best part of a year, everything seemed to be going well. Annabel was cheerful, but not overly so, she was working, and sex had become as he had always hoped — fun, innovative and, most importantly, loving. What went wrong? He tried, he really did, to believe that it was a pill failure, but deep down he knew that it wasn't and that she was responsible for stopping it. The early part of the pregnancy was easy. She felt well, there was no morning sickness and she appeared blissfully happy. He believed that he had managed to hide his fears and worries about her.

The discovery that she was expecting twins seemed a bonus, even more so when it had been shown that they were of different genders, which, he thought, might persuade her that a further pregnancy would be both unwise and unnecessary.

After the birth by Caesarean section, though, Annabel literally turned her face to the wall. She didn't want to set eyes on the babies, let alone feed them, and she became virtually mute. The best psychiatric opinions were sought and every conceivable treatment tried and all that achieved was the worst possible outcome. They had moved into the big house and Richard had managed to find a girl from the village who was prepared to move in and look after the twins. Annabel seemed slowly to be coming out of her apathetic state, but tragically it only served to provide her with the direction and energy to kill herself in a particularly terrible way.

* * *

'Richard couldn't bring himself to tell me what she had done, but somehow or other, with the help of his parents and the girl, he somehow managed to cope. That girl was only sixteen, but she took charge of the babies, proving herself to be a natural mother and all seemed to be going really well, but then his mother had a massive stroke and after she died, his father, who had found the increasingly noisy and quarrelsome twins too much for him, decided to move into the flat in the club he owned in South Kensington.

'The twins proved to be a real handful, always fighting over something, and Adam's strength and aggression was more than balanced by Kate's superior intelligence and greater determination. If he played some nasty trick on her, she played an even nastier one back on him. They had also turned on Meg, the girl from the village, refusing to do her bidding and repeatedly telling her that she wasn't their mother, so there!

'For a time they went to the local primary school, but then, after his father, too, had died, Farrant decided that different boarding prep schools were the only answer as he couldn't ask Meg to put up with them together any longer. It worked out better than he could have hoped. They both did extremely well academically and Adam showed great promise as a games player. As for the school holidays, the two of them seemed to have reached a state of armed neutrality and got on adequately by the simple expedient of seeing as little of each other as possible. Adam went off to adventure camps whenever possible and spent some of the holidays staying with like-minded friends from his school and Kate went up to London with her father and as often as he could, when he was not too busy at his club, he went with her to the nearby museums in South Kensington. He also took them on visits abroad, including the USA, where he had many contacts.

'As to their time here,' Barclay said, 'it could hardly be said to have been more successful. Adam turned out to be one of the best all-round games players we have ever had here and seemed to find an acceptable outlet to his aggression on the games field. However, there was one episode on the rugby field when he upended one of the opposition's best players, when he was some way off the ball, and damned near broke his neck.'

'What did you do about that?' Sinclair asked.

'I told him that if he ever did anything like that again, he would never play rugby, or for that matter, any other game for the college again.'

'And did it work?'

Barclay smiled. 'I meant it and more importantly he knew that I did, so I think I can say that it did.'

'And did you tell his father?'

'No and the reason was that I wanted to stamp my own authority on that sort of thing and I was quite sure that Richard would support me should the need arise. I'm quite sure, too, that Adam knew that too. The real crunch, though, came at the Founder's Day celebrations here, which for as long as anyone can remember has a traditional pattern. There is a cricket match against the old boys, a speech from the headmaster outlining the events of the previous year, some words from the chairman of the board and a lecture given by one of our distinguished old alumni. That year it was given by Richard Farrant and very dramatic it was. He gave an illustrated talk on extreme sports, with spectacular video clips, not only of his area of expertise, powerboat racing, but with aerobatics, sky diving and rock climbing. It was done very well, without any hint of showing off, and he pointed out that such things weren't everyone's cup of tea but that there were parallels in many other fields of endeavour, physical or intellectual. The important thing, he said, is to make the best of what talents and interests you have and that there was every bit as much merit in being a good citizen in the broadest sense of that term as excelling in some narrow field of endeavour, such as sports or intellectual activity. He might so easily have sounded pompous and pleased with himself, but he didn't and it went down very well.

'I had already sat with him while watching the cricket match and that was really the start of it as far as I was concerned, although the real bombshell came when he asked if I would meet him at his hotel for tea the following day as he had some very important matters to discuss with me. I will try to put the various events in some sort of order, starting with the cricket match, so that they will be, I hope, comprehensible.'

★ ★ ★

'I'm very much looking forward to seeing Rachel Lewis bowl,' Richard Farrant said to the headmaster, as they sat side by side on the top tier of seats in front of the pavilion, watching the two umpires walking out towards the pitch. 'I happen to know Jim Alexander, the coach, well and he had a word with me about her earlier today. It seems that he's spent a lot of time with her in the nets and he considers that she could be really good, well worth a regular place in the team. He even went as far as to say that if she continues to work hard at it, she might well make the England women's team in the future. That's hardly the view that Adam takes. He thinks that women are taking over everything and things were much better when they were chained to the sink. The boy's a silly ass. My view is that if she is good enough to get into the college team on merit, then good luck to her.'

'I agree,' Barclay said. 'I haven't seen her play yet, but Trent, the master in charge of cricket, also has good things to say about her.'

They had to wait a long time to watch Rachel Lewis bowl. The match was forty overs a side, with any bowler having a maximum of eight overs each, and, having won the toss, the Old Brantlians put the college into bat.

'Not too bad,' Farrant said after the boys had managed to score 175 for eight in their allocation of overs, 'but I doubt if it will be enough. It was all Adam's fault. He was going so well and there was no need for him to have a rush of blood to the head with all of fifteen overs to go. No doubt he'll be pleased with his fifty-five, but he should have gone on from there.'

Barclay knew exactly what Farrant meant. Adam had taken a wild swipe at an outswinger from one of the old boys' medium-pace bowlers, his foot wasn't anywhere near the pitch of the ball and it went steepling up almost vertically and the wicket keeper had taken a comfortable catch.

Farrant shook his head. 'That was quite typical of him and many's the time I've told him that he'll never be any good until he learns that one can't hit every ball to the boundary.'

After lunch, the old boys' side made steady progress and at 150 for six with ten overs left, it looked as if they were going to win comfortably.

'Why the hell doesn't Adam give that girl a bowl?' Farrant said. 'It was quite obvious from the college's innings that the spinners are proving much more of a handful on this wicket than the seamers.'

Ten minutes and three overs later, Adam at last threw the ball to her. Through the binoculars that Farrant had passed to him,

Barclay could see that Rachel was desperately nervous, passing the ball rapidly from hand to hand and biting her lip. Her first delivery was woefully short and the opposition's top batsman, who was already sixty-five not out, dismissed it with a powerful pull shot to the square leg boundary. The headmaster focused on Adam Farrant, who was fielding at mid off and who had thrown up his arms in an exaggerated gesture of annoyance, staring in the girl's direction and shaking his head.

The girl's second ball was on a good length and the man facing her played it back carefully straight back to her. The following one was quicker, pitched on middle and leg and as the man played forward, it spun sharply, just missed the edge of his bat and clipped the top of the off stump, dislodging the bail.

'What a peach of a delivery!' Farrant said, clapping enthusiastically. 'As I said, that fool of a son of mine should have put her on at least half an hour ago.'

Barclay didn't reply, watching through the binoculars as Adam Farrant ran up to her and gave her a hard slap on her bottom. The girl whirled round towards him and said something that brought a smirk to his face. If Farrant Senior had seen it, he didn't say anything and when Barclay turned towards him, he saw that the man was filling in his scorecard.

At the end of the next over, after the right-handed off spinner at the other end had conceded ten runs, including a massive six over long-on, Rachel Lewis started another over, there now being only four of them left and nine runs needed for the old boys to win. Her first two deliveries spun sharply across the batsman's forward prod, just missing the edge of the bat and with the third, he played back, expecting the ball to break from leg to off. It didn't. It had top spin on it, went straight on and hit the man's pads right in front of the stumps.

'That was brilliant,' Farrant said. 'Really well thought out. I was going to say that she lacked variety, but I was quite wrong.'

Rachel got one more wicket in her next over. The batsman advanced down the pitch, trying to finish the match with a six. The girl obviously saw him coming, bowling the ball both quicker and shorter. He missed it and was stumped easily. With still six runs required and the last man in, Adam Farrant brought on the college's fast bowler at the other end. It didn't work. Obviously nervous, the boy started with a no ball, was then hit for a two and then a four and that was that.

'What a good match that was,' Barclay said,

joining in with the applause as the two batsmen walked off, followed by the college team.

'Yes,' agreed Richard. 'I have to confess that I thought that Jim Alexander was overdoing his praise for that girl, but I was quite wrong. She shows exceptional promise.'

5

A few minutes after four o'clock the following day, David Barclay drove into the car park and went in through the swing doors of the hotel. Richard Farrant, who had been sitting with his two children in the lobby, rose to his feet and smiled at him.

'Thanks for coming, David. The hotel has a small conference room just over there and I suggest we go there.' He turned to the boy and girl. 'As I told you, Kate, there are some college matters I want to discuss with you and Mr Barclay, and Adam, perhaps you wouldn't mind waiting here. We shouldn't be too long.'

There was a circular table in the conference room and when they were seated, Farrant looked across at the headmaster.

'There have been some very disquieting events going on here over the last few weeks and I'll ask Kate to repeat what she told me yesterday.'

The young woman sat very still for a few moments and then began.

★ ★ ★

Kate Farrant was having a cup of tea with Pauline Cassidy, her housemistress, as she did every week on Saturday afternoons when they discussed any minor problems that had cropped up during the previous week. There had been an instance of bullying, not the first one involving a particular girl, and they had decided that it was time for her parents to be brought in and that the coming Founder's Day weekend, when they would be visiting, would be the best time.

'Right,' Miss Cassidy said. 'Anything else you'd like to bring up, Kate?'

Before she had time to reply they both heard someone running along the corridor and then a loud knock.

The woman got up and opened the door. 'How many times have I told you not to run up the stairs and along the corridor, Stephanie?' she said. 'What is it?'

'It's Sophie, Miss Cassidy. She's cut her finger on the cake knife. It's really bad and she's gone very pale.'

'All right, I'd better go down.'

'Do you want me to come, too?'

'No, thank you, Kate. There are some other things I want to talk to you about and, as you well know, Sophie's a bit of a tragedy queen. I shouldn't be too long and I'll ring you on the internal phone if I need your help.'

126

The call came only a few minutes later. 'It is quite a nasty cut and it's going to need stitches. I'll take her down to the local casualty department in my car. Stephanie will come with me — she's good with the silly girl. Would you mind bringing my bag down? I'll need my mobile and car keys and then perhaps you'd wait in my study so that I can give you a ring when I know what the hospital have to say. Please feel free to watch TV if there's anything of interest on.'

After the housemistress had gone and Kate had calmed everyone down and settled the junior girls under the supervision of one of the prefects for their coursework, Kate went back up the stairs. Being no devotee of quiz and antiques shows, she pressed the play button on the video recorder under the TV. Later she was to think that one of the reasons she did it was that she had her suspicions about Pauline Cassidy and maybe the woman liked looking at video porn to do with young girls. It wasn't only that she quite unnecessarily used to supervise the shower sessions and her gaze only too obviously wandered in directions it most certainly should not have done, but she was also prone to putting her arm round their shoulders at other times in a way that might have been construed as just a motherly gesture — but Kate was quite sure that it was more than that. The images on the screen flickered and then cleared and Kate immediately recognized both the girl and where she was. The camera had been aimed at the mirror above the basin in the bathroom and the strikingly pretty girl with the neat figure was looking over her shoulder at her reflection in the mirror. Her firm buttocks were disfigured by three purple welts and an inch-long scab where two of the strokes had crossed and very gently the girl touched it with her forefinger.

Kate was not the sort of person to be easily shaken, but when the images faded to be replaced by a blank screen, she stood there immobile for some time, checked the number on the counter, then wound the tape to the very beginning before pressing the play button again. There were other images of girls, all of whom she recognized, and worst of all one of herself.

After she had returned the position of the tape to the one it had been in before she started to look at it, Kate Farrant sat down by the desk for the next half hour, deep in thought, and by the time Miss Cassidy had rung from the hospital to say that the girl was being stitched and that she would not be back for at least another forty minutes, as instructed she pulled the door to on its Yale lock, knowing what she was going to do.

★ ★ ★

Rachel Lewis had thought that the nightmare was over at last. The marks of her beating had faded to thin brown lines, all the stiffness had gone and she was gaining confidence in her attempts in the nets to increase the amount of spin on the cricket ball without losing accuracy. Despite the coach's encouragement, though, she knew perfectly well that it was one thing to be able to do it in the nets with Jim Alexander standing by her and quite another to repeat it in an important game. The appearance of Adam Farrant, though, just as she was leaving the nets, spoiled it all. Her tormentor was leering at her and to think that he had another year as captain.

In her room, after a long bath, she did her best to make a start on her essay and was studying the notes she had already made when she heard the soft tap on the door and gave a start.

'Come in.'

'Sorry to disturb you, Rachel, may I have a word?'

'Of course,' she said, starting to get up as

she saw Kate Farrant standing in the doorway.

'Don't move, I'll perch on the side of your bed.' There was a long pause while the head of the house looked at her very directly. 'I have uncovered some very unsettling matters going on in this house that involve both of us. The fact is that Miss Cassidy is a very disturbed person and she has taken advantage of her position here to satisfy her perverted tastes. She has hidden a video camera in one of our bathrooms and has taken pictures of both you and me, amongst others, in there, which are on tape. I haven't yet decided exactly what to do about it, but in order to do the best I can, I need to know exactly what happened to you and why. You have obviously been on the receiving end of three very hard strokes from a cane and I'm pretty sure that it came from one of the crossed pair that are attached to the wall above the fireplace in the college prefects' room. On my way here I had a look at them and it's quite obvious that although they are both still there, they have recently been moved and there is a small stain on one of them, which is almost certainly your blood. It's not only that, I remember how ill you looked one morning at breakfast and that my brother made some remark to you, which I didn't hear, but obviously upset you. Now, if I am to help you over this and at the same time deal with Miss Cassidy, I need you to tell me the exact truth of what happened to you and why. All right?'

'Will my parents or the head be told about all this?'

'I can't guarantee it, but what passes between you and your parents has nothing to do with me. However, Miss Cassidy cannot be allowed to continue to behave in the way she has and my fear is that she may also be abusing some of the other girls physically, although I have no direct evidence of it. Now, I promise to do my very best for you, but if I am going to be able to sort this mess out as I just said, I need you to tell me exactly what happened and that means leaving nothing out.'

Rachel hesitated, but not for very long. What choice did she really have? One thing she was not going to do, though, was to tell anyone about the person she had been with that night in the gym nor, she swore to herself, would she ever speak to him again. And then there were her parents. She knew just how expensive the fees at the college were and what a struggle it had been for them to find the money and she also resolved there and then that never ever would she let them down again.

'All right,' she said, looking very directly at the young woman sitting on the bed.

★ ★ ★

Rachel Lewis gave Rob's hand a gentle squeeze, leaned over to kiss him and then, after one last drag on the spliff, lay back on the padded mat. Only the faintest light from the new moon was coming through the large windows of the pavilion and it seemed to her as if she was in an enchanted land. Although she had never been in one, it was as she imagined it must be like to be in a flotation chamber, a sensation of total relaxation and delicious warmth that went right through her as she went over the sequence of events.

There had been the long wait until her bedside clock, with its luminous hands and dial showed ten to two, followed by the noiseless dressing in a shirt, briefs, tracksuit, socks and trainers. That was followed by the careful descent of the staircase, avoidance of the third one down, which creaked, and the very gentle easing up of the window in the downstairs lavatory next to the outside door. The space was narrow, but she was slim and agile and she had done it several times before.

The anticipation of what was to follow was

almost unbearable as she skirted the games field behind the screen of trees and then climbed into the pavilion through the window at the back and into the shower room. She had often wondered how frequently that way in had been used over the 150 years since the building had been constructed. To the casual glance it looked as if it was firmly closed, but late that afternoon Rob had released the catch locking the two halves of the window together and it was the work of a moment to slide the two halves apart and climb through the gap at the bottom, using the log that Rob had left outside as a step.

Rob had been waiting for her and after a quick kiss, she whispered in his ear, 'It's my turn tonight.' She pushed him down on to the padded mat, then, when she had slipped all her clothes off, eased his tracksuit and pants off and very gently lowered herself down so that he slid into her. She could hardly see him in the dim light filtering through the front windows of the gym, but felt his growing excitement until her own overcame everything else and she hardly knew where she was or what she was doing.

What followed was as good, just different. Sitting side by side on the mat against the wall bars with their clothes back on and feeling the cannabis taking over, Rachel couldn't remember ever having been more relaxed or happy.

The shock of the blinding light shining straight into her eyes snapped her into full consciousness.

'Well, well, well! What have we here?'

They both recognized the male voice at once and started to get to their feet.

'Stay exactly where you are. Sex and pot, is it? If the headmaster and mistress get to hear of this, you'll be out of this place by the weekend. No excuses, no appeal. What do you suppose your parents are going to say about that? I tell you what, I'll make a deal with the two of you. In days gone by it would have been six of the very best on the bare for each of you and that would have been the end of it. What do you think?'

The figure advanced a couple of steps and brought the crook-handled cane into the light.

'Well, what's your answer?'

The boy beside her struggled to his feet and took half a step forward. 'It's all my fault and I'll take both lots if you let her go.'

Rachel could hear the shakiness in his voice and made a sudden decision — she just couldn't let that happen and, legs trembling, rose unsteadily to stand by him, taking his hand in hers and giving it a gentle squeeze.

'No, it's my fault just as much as his. We're both in this together.'

'Very well. Usually it's ladies first, but this time it'll be the other way round.'

'I'm not leaving her alone with you.'

'Oh yes you are, unless you want me to wake the head up.' There was a long pause. 'Well, what's the verdict?' He shone the light straight at the boy's face and after a moment or two saw the almost imperceptible nod. 'Right, bend over and grip the wall bars. No, not there, lower down.'

He reversed the cane, prodding the girl in the stomach with the handle. 'You sit down right here, watch what's happening and don't you so much as think of moving a muscle.'

Rachel began to shiver as she saw Rob gripping the bars tightly, then winced as she heard the whistle and then the sharp crack as the cane came down.

There was a long pause and then the torch was shone straight at her. 'I told you to watch and if I catch you shutting your eyes again, he'll get an extra stroke every time you do so.'

Not once did Rob cry out, but when at last it was over, she could see him shivering violently, so violently that the bar was rattling.

'Now get out and take that filthy thing and the remains of that spliff with you and don't even think of waiting for the girl outside.

Should you do so, she'll get double.'

He picked up the condom with the tip of the cane, held it out and then waited until the boy had gone through the door into the changing room.

'Now, little girl, it's your turn and, tell you what, I'll do a deal with you. Take all your clothes off, let me see you, all of you and I'll let you off with three.'

Rachel hesitated, but only for a moment. What if he does see me, she thought. It won't hurt and it'll make me despise him even more.

'All right, but you're not to touch me.'

'What makes you think I'd want to after what you've been doing, you filthy slut? Now, get on with it.'

He didn't spare her, forcing her to take up several utterly degrading positions, and while she did so, bringing the light to within inches of her.

The pain, when it came, was indescribable, worse than she could have imagined, and she was near to fainting when the last vicious blow landed. The one thing she held on to was that she wasn't going to give him the satisfaction of making a sound, although she wasn't able to prevent the violent trembling of her thighs.

'Now, get out!'

She felt the sweat on her forehead and was feeling light-headed, but somehow managed to pull on her briefs, shirt, tracksuit and trainers and get back into the house. It was only the following evening when she was lying face down on her bed that she realized how lucky she had been. The very idea of that would have seemed utterly ridiculous only a few hours earlier, but now she had no doubt about it. It had been a real sacrifice for her parents to send her to the college and to have been thrown out would have hurt them deeply and she somehow knew that however good a face they put on it, it would alter their relationship for ever. It wasn't only that; it had been the height of her ambition to play for the boys' first eleven and when they heard that she had been selected for the match against the old alumni on Founder's Day in two weeks time, they had promised to come down to watch. There was only one possible way to deal with it and that was to put it all behind her, break with Rob, even to the extent of not even talking to him again and make the very best she could of the rest of the time at the college.

Getting through the first day had been by no means easy. By the time she had got back to the bathroom on her floor after her beating, some blood had seeped through her briefs and tracksuit and after she had peeled them off, she stood on the stool and looked at herself in the mirror above the basin. It was the last vicious stroke that had split the skin where it had crossed the other two and where the tip had bitten into the top of her right thigh was still stinging. Very gently, she patted the still-oozing area with a tissue and when it had stopped, she washed out her soiled clothes and put them in the airing cupboard.

Setting her alarm to ensure that she wouldn't be late for breakfast, she lay face down on a towel on top of her bed in case she turned over during the remainder of the night. She didn't actually expect to sleep — but whatever the reason perhaps, she thought, it might have been a mixture of reaction to what had happened, exhaustion or the effects of the cannabis — she was fast asleep when the alarm woke her and found that she had hardly moved.

Rachel was very stiff, but she managed to walk along the corridor forcing herself not to limp and in the bathroom mirror she saw to her relief that there had been no recurrence of the bleeding. She was well aware, though, that the first big test would be when she had to sit down for breakfast. Before the war, feeding at the college had been in the individual houses, but with rationing, all the main meals were provided centrally in one of the large halls with the kitchen partitioned off at the side. It was some 200 yards from Rachel's house and that proved no problem, but as she was standing in the queue in the serving area, Kate Farrant came up to her.

'Are you all right, Rachel? You look very pale.'

'I'm fine, thank you, Kate. Just a touch of the usual.'

The head of her house nodded and moved a short distance away, while Rachel, determined neither to limp towards the long table nor wince when she lowered herself on to the bench beside it, then looked up sharply when she heard the mocking voice and saw Adam Farrant standing just behind her, a sinister smile on his face.

'Hope you're ready for a long practice at the nets after tea today, Rachel. The big match is less than two weeks off, as you well know, and we're relying on you to put on a good show.'

'I'll be there.'

Bastard, she thought, as he walked away, smirking. She didn't believe that he would report her to the headmaster and mistress, but it was only too obvious that he was going to milk the situation for all it was worth.

The session in the nets later that day was

an ordeal. She was so stiff that her normal relaxed approach when she was approaching the crease was impossible and she was unable to get into her normal rhythm.

'What's wrong, Rachel? You're not yourself at all today,' the cricket coach said.

'I'm not feeling too well,' she replied.

The man looked at her with concern. 'It's no good soldiering on if you're out of sorts. Why not go and have a lie down? A couple of days off won't do you any harm.'

She could see Adam Farrant smirking in the background and, ignoring him, she went back to her house and took another look at herself in the bathroom mirror. The bruising had spread and looked even more spectacular. It brought to her mind the film *Black Box*, which she had seen on DVD with some friends during the previous holidays and had so enjoyed. She vividly remembered the young female singer who had joined the Dutch resistance at the time when the country was about to be liberated. She had penetrated the Nazi headquarters, had been suspected of being a collaborator when the British forces had arrived, and was paraded with others in front of a jeering crowd. Ordered to strip, she refused to do so and after her clothes had been ripped off was brutally beaten and other humiliations heaped on her. The young woman hadn't cried out or pleaded for mercy and her ordeal was only ended when a British officer arrived and she was rescued.

Rachel hadn't cried out either, nor had she pleaded for mercy, but when she was back in her room, the reality hit her. Her situation was far removed from that of the brave young Dutch woman. All right, she had taken her punishment and humiliation bravely, but it wasn't as if she had been tricked into having sex and smoking pot. The whole thing had been as much her responsibility as that of Rob.

Why was her sexual impulse so strong it was almost unbearable at times? Had she no self control nor respect for the sacrifices her parents had made in sending her to a private school, which they had only been able to finance by giving up holidays and other comforts? How, too, was she going to be able to face them when they came to Founder's Day, specially to watch her play cricket?

Rachel loved cricket and taking inspiration from the girl who had already played for her public school first eleven and for England in a one-day match at Lord's, she was determined not to waste the first opportunity she was going to have to do the same at Brantley, despite the opposition of some of the boys and masters. She was tall and flexible and was able to spin her left arm deliveries quite sharply if there was any help from the pitch, and was very accurate, having put in hours of practice in the nets. Jim Alexander, the professional, had been a spin bowler himself and had put down a white card on a length and made her work at it until she was able to hit it regularly. The boys on the team didn't like several things about her: she was younger than any of the other players, she worked harder on her game and they were envious of the attention that Jim paid to her.

They had tried bullying her, too. Just before one of the trial matches between the first and second elevens, the coach found her struggling to release the laces of her boots — which had been tied together in a tight and complicated series of knots — with her nail file.

'Don't worry, lass,' he said, 'I'll cut them off for you and I've got some spares in my room. I won't be a moment.'

'Fancy her then, do you, Jim?'

Adam Farrant was standing at the open door with a smirk on his face.

Jim Alexander picked up the boots with one hand and advanced towards the boy, staring at him unblinkingly.

'Why not give me a hand with these boots?

You wouldn't want to delay the start of the match, would you?'

In one swift movement, Alexander caught hold of the boy's left wrist and forced it up behind his back, propelling him towards his workroom on the other side of the pavilion.

'The headmaster will hear about this,' the boy said through gritted teeth.

'Yes, he will, won't he? As it happens, I wasn't only thinking about the headmaster. I'm quite sure you know that your father was one of the best schoolboy cricketers of his time and went on to play for his university and had some games for the Durham county side. What you may not know is that we played together and he was instrumental in helping me get this job. He is coming to watch the match on Saturday week as well as giving a lecture and I don't think he'd take kindly to that remark or the way you've been behaving towards Rachel here. He has and always has had very clear ideas about sportsmanship and any more of that, or failing to support or use her talents, he'll hear about it. She may be inexperienced, but even so, she's the best bowler we've got by some margin and it's as well that you remember that.'

After that, she was left alone; that is, until the events in the gym.

6

'So that's it, is it?' Barclay said, looking intently at Kate Farrant, who returned his gaze without looking away, or even blinking.

'Yes. I thought it best to do nothing further about all this until I had the opportunity to speak to my father and you, sir.'

'So Miss Cassidy doesn't know what you discovered on her tape recorder or in the bathroom?'

'Not as far as I know and I think it very unlikely. Her manner towards me hasn't changed and I have been careful to behave in exactly the same way towards her as I have always done since I became head of the house.'

'And what about Rachel Lewis?' Richard Farrant said.

'I believe everything she said. In my work on chemistry, I have some knowledge of forensic tests and I found traces of blood on one of those canes in the college prefects' room and no doubt both Rachel's and Adam's DNA will be on it, too. I also ran a test on the big mat in the gym where Rachel and the boy had sex and a stain tested positive for semen.'

'Do you know the name of the boy Sarah was involved with?' asked her father.

'No. She wouldn't say.'

'Any other questions, Barclay?'

'Not for the moment.'

'Right. Kate, would you wait outside and ask Adam to come in, please?'

Adam Farrant had the suspicion of a smile on his face as he came into the room but that was soon obliterated when his father pointed towards the chair that his sister had just vacated and said:

'Adam, take that supercilious grin off your face and sit down there.'

'What's all this about, Dad?'

'You'll very soon find out. I understand that about two weeks ago, you beat Rachel Lewis in the gym after she had had sex with one of the boys and the two of them were smoking cannabis. You also made her strip and expose herself.'

Farrant looked at his son very directly, who held his gaze for a moment and then looked away, glancing in the headmaster's direction, whose expression hadn't changed.

'I suppose it was that bitch who told you. I'll . . .'

'Adam!'

The boy started to get up from his chair,

but shrank back when he saw the expression on his father's face.

'Rachel didn't say anything until she was confronted with the evidence, part of which was the blood traces which were found on the cane from the college prefects' room which you used.'

The boy suddenly seemed to realize the full implications of what his father had said and all the colour went out of his cheeks.

'She asked for it. I found her in the gym having had sex and smoking pot with Rob Pearce from my house and decided to punish them both rather than reporting them to the head and getting them expelled.'

'So that's what you did, was it? Now, you'd better tell your side of the story and I strongly advise you to leave nothing out.'

There was a long pause, then without looking up he began: 'I heard Robert Pearce, one of the sixteen-year-olds in my house getting up during the night it happened. I followed him round the edge of the cricket ground and saw him climb in through one of the side windows of the pavilion. I waited outside and when he didn't reappear after fifteen minutes or so, I went in that way myself. I found him and Rachel sitting on the mat in the gym, smoking pot and it was obvious that they had had sex as well. I then

146

offered them the choice of the cane or being reported to the headmaster.'

'I understand that they were both wearing their tracksuits when you found them and that you made the girl both strip and expose herself to you.'

'Did that lying bitch tell you that, too?'

'You say anything like that again and I'll smash your face in,' warned Richard.

Adam Farrant glanced at his father, suddenly seemed to realize that the man meant it and shrank back in his chair.

'The evidence was quite clear. Traces of her blood were found on the cane that you used and would not have got there had she been wearing her tracksuit.'

'What cane?'

'You know very well. The one you took from the college prefects' room and then put back. Should it prove necessary, both your fingerprints and DNA will no doubt be found on it, as well as that of the girl.'

Beads of sweat were standing out on the boy's forehead as his father got up and stood in front of him.

'Now, you'll tell me exactly what happened.'

Slowly and with relentless questioning from his father, the story came out. He had followed the boy on an earlier occasion and then found the boy and girl smoking pot in the pavilion. He resented Rachel deeply, firstly because he didn't want a mere girl playing on his cricket team and secondly because she was obviously a very talented bowler and was getting more than her fair share of the coaching. He knew that if he reported her to the headmaster she would be expelled, but that could wait. If they did it again it would give him the opportunity to humiliate her and, better than that, to achieve his favourite fantasy of caning a naked girl.

It worked out better than he could have hoped. He kept a watch on the boy and when he saw him leave the house a week later, went straight to the college prefects' room, took down one of the canes and set off for the pavilion. The whole event exceeded his wildest expectations. They had taken their time and when he got there, they were still locked together on the mat. He watched as they finally stirred, dressed and then began to smoke the spliffs and then he was able to achieve his ambition.

It would have been even better if either of them, particularly the girl, had pleaded with him, but they hadn't and, for his part, he hadn't spared either of them. Best of all, he had seen Rachel Lewis, the snooty bitch, every single bit of her.

Farrant looked at his son with utter contempt. 'Indecent assault, grievous bodily harm, not on one person, but two. Tell me, Barclay, what is the likely sentence for that in the courts?'

'Minimum of two years in a young offenders' institution, I'd say.'

'And no doubt the others in that institution might well pick on a toffee-nosed, upper-class twit, might they not?'

'More than likely, I would say.'

Farrant nodded. 'And it would also mean no Sandhurst, no career in the army and being disinherited, wouldn't it? Now, go into the cloakroom over there and wait while I have a word with Mr Barclay and there you'll stay until we've finished our discussion.'

Farrant followed his son across the room, closed the door of the cloakroom and put a chair under its handle, then sat down again and looked the headmaster straight in the eye.

'Adam's behaviour has been utterly despicable and you may have noticed that he slapped the girl's backside really hard when she took her first wicket. I propose to remove him from the college today and take him to the States with me. It so happens that a year or two ago I gave a talk to a boot camp for unruly boys and I was very impressed with what I saw and the results they achieved. He will go there and if, as I hope, it instils some remorse and sense into him, he might just be able to achieve his ambition of going to Sandhurst. As you know, he has just taken his A levels and it seems likely that he will do well in them. As far as a reference from the college is concerned, should that be required, I'll leave that to you, and whatever action you propose to take over the boy and girl involved in all this and, of course, Kate's housemistress.'

★　★　★

'Are you all right, love? You look so tired; you mustn't overdo it, you know,' Rachel's mother said to her as they were leaving.

'I'm fine, thanks, Mum, it's just all the excitement.'

'Your father and I are so proud of you. We already knew how well your work was going, but the cricket is something else.'

'Yes,' her father added with a smile. 'Mr Farrant made a point of talking to us after the match and told us how impressed he was with your bowling. He even said that if you practised hard, there was no reason why you shouldn't reach the very top, even playing for the England women's team.'

'He said that?'

'He most certainly did and he really meant it. I also respect his opinion. You may not know that he played cricket for Durham University himself and even had a few games for the county.'

Surely, Rachel thought, if Mr Barclay knew anything about what had happened to her in the gym, he would have spoken to them before they left. After checking that there was no sign of a camera in the second bathroom, she had a long soak, feeling the tension gradually draining away. She was back in her room, trying to concentrate on the essay that she was due to hand in the following week when there was a soft knock on the door. It hadn't sounded in the least threatening, but even so a shiver went right down her back.

'Come in.'

Kate Farrant was standing at the entrance and gave her a smile.

'Sorry to disturb you, but I thought you'd like to know that my father has taken Adam away from the college and he won't be coming back. I haven't time to explain the details and I don't know what the headmaster is going to do about Miss Cassidy because he wants to see you right away. I don't know what he's going to say to you, but my father's advice was that you should be totally honest about it and leave nothing out at all. My father never says anything he doesn't mean.'

'What about the headmistress?'

'I think you'll find that Miss Sandon is too occupied with deciding what to do about Miss Cassidy to worry about you as well.'

Rachel never knew how she managed to walk the few hundred yards to the headmaster's house — it was far worse than waiting to start an exam, going into bat or even the time when she went back to her house after the events in the gym. It was Mrs Barclay who answered her ring on the front door and looked at her with an anxious expression on her face.

'Are you all right, dear, you look as pale as a ghost.'

'Yes, thank you, Mrs Barclay.'

'If you're really sure, I'll take you up.'

The woman knocked on the door of his study and opened it in response to his 'come in'. 'Rachel is here, David.'

'Good. Thank you, dear. Ask her to come in, would you?'

The headmaster made a gesture towards the chair in front of his desk and then went to his own behind it.

'I already know something of what happened to you in the gym, but I want to hear from you every last detail. Is that quite clear?'

Rachel nodded, not trusting herself to speak for a moment, then began. The man on the other side of the desk never dropped his eyes from her face as she described what had happened. 'How many times had you done it before that night?'

'Twice, sir.'

'Both this term?'

'Yes, sir.'

'I want you to explain why you did it.'

She did try, but it sounded so stupid and ridiculous to herself, let alone, she thought, to the headmaster, that it only came out hesitantly with long pauses. The truth, as she did her best to voice, was that it all started when she first noticed the boy. She was running towards the nets, so as not to be late for her bowling practice with the cricket coach, when she tripped on a stone at the edge of the cricket field and fell heavily, twisting her knee. She was sitting on the grass, massaging it gently, when the boy knelt down beside her.

'What bad luck! Does it hurt a lot?'

'Not too bad.'

The extraordinary feeling, that caused her to give an involuntary gasp when he rolled up her trouser leg and gently put his finger on her knee, was unlike anything she had experienced before. She knew what it was, though. How could she not when it was so embarrassingly localized? That was how it had started and it went on from there with little smiles, seemingly accidental meetings and then the first kiss and other intimate contacts when they met behind the pavilion one Sunday afternoon. It was he who finally persuaded her to meet him inside the building in the small hours one Saturday night. There had been the anxiety and excitement of getting out of her house and climbing in through the side window of the pavilion, which he had left open for her, and the fear that what followed would hurt and that it wouldn't work for her. The boy sensed it and said that if they had a smoke it would relax her, take away all the anxiety and make it just wonderful. She hadn't believed him, but in truth it had been utterly amazing, dwarfing her own previous clumsy and guilty attempts at achieving the same ends.

'So it was he who suggested and supplied the cannabis?' asked Barclay. Rachel nodded. 'And why did you agree to undress for Adam Farrant?'

Rachel looked directly across at the headmaster over the desk. 'Because he told me he'd let me off with three strokes if I did and I had seen how hard he beat my boyfriend. I didn't have the courage to take six strokes myself and I have been deeply ashamed about that ever since.'

'Have you seen the other boy since?'

'Only in the distance and I promised myself that I would never do it with him or see him again.'

'But Adam Farrant didn't leave you alone?'

'No, he sneered at me at breakfast the following morning and made obscene gestures to me on other occasions when he knew that no one was looking and hit me really hard on the bottom with his hand when I took my first wicket at the match against the old boys.'

'I see. Are you prepared to promise me that you won't smoke cannabis ever again, let alone here, and that you won't have sex or even talk to that other boy on the college premises?'

Rachel didn't hesitate. 'Yes, sir. I don't intend to see him ever again here or anywhere else.'

'I know who he is — Adam told his father — and I propose to speak to him in exactly the same way as I have to you and expect to receive the same promises. Mr Farrant has already taken Adam away and he will not be allowed to enter the college premises again and you have nothing to fear from him. Now, you are not to speak about this to anyone, anyone at all, either here or at home, now or at any time in the future. Is that quite clear?'

'Yes, sir.'

'Now, that's quite enough from me. As far as I know, the only other person who knows exactly what happened to you is Kate Farrant; I will be speaking to her as well and I trust her completely to keep silent about all this.

'You may be wondering about Miss Cassidy. All I am prepared to say about her is that she broke her trust as a schoolteacher, that she has already left the college and that she will not be allowed to work with children again.'

★ ★ ★

David Barclay shook his head slightly. 'That was it, really. We were lucky that it was nearly the end of term and it also helped me that Miss Sandon was retiring at the same time. I did try to keep her in touch with what was going on and involve her in some of the decisions, but she was beginning to lose it a bit mentally and I don't think she took it all in.'

'What happened to Miss Cassidy?' asked Sinclair.

'That worried me as much if not more than anything else. In return for not reporting the matter to the police, I told her that she would only be allowed to leave with her personal effects, which I would be checking. I also made a photocopy of the important pages in her passport; we already had her national insurance number and details of her bank account in the office. Finally, I told her that she was never to work with children again, either as a teacher or any other capacity, of either sex.'

'How did she react to that?'

'She was in a state of shock, I believe, and hardly said a word.'

'Any idea what happened to her?'

'I did give her mother, whom she had given as her next of kin, a ring at the start of the next term. I told her that we had found some textbooks belonging to her in a cupboard in her old form room and I thought it would be as good excuse as any for trying to find out what she was doing.'

'And?'

'I didn't have any luck. The woman hadn't heard from her daughter since she left the school.'

'Did you follow that up in any way?'

The man shook his head. 'No, I didn't, and I suppose I should have done, but, to be honest, I couldn't face the hassle and decided to let sleeping dogs lie. If I stirred things up, I reasoned, it would almost certainly create major problems for Farrant Senior, the college and young Rachel Lewis. I assure you I am not leaving out my own personal worries, either.'

'What happened to Rachel?'

'She went to Loughborough and then became a regular member of the English women's cricket team; they were playing in Australia recently. As far as the Farrants are concerned, I saw Richard at some of the governors meetings and he told me about Kate's first in chemistry at Imperial College and that she had also qualified as a chartered accountant, but all that was a long time ago.'

'And you were satisfied that Kate Farrant's role in all this was completely above board?' Sarah asked.

'Absolutely. She was as straight as a die, just like her father. Why do you ask?'

Sarah smiled. 'I just wanted your opinion, that's all, and inevitably I was wondering how worried she might have been about Adam wanting to seek his revenge.'

'Both Richard Farrant and I were careful not even to hint to Adam that she was directly involved in the discovery of that tape. I also had the greatest respect for her honesty and probity, as I've already indicated.'

'Do you have the address of Miss Cassidy's mother, by any chance?' Sinclair asked.

'I'm not sure. I do have all the details of current staff here, but those from the past are with the archivist. Why not go to see him? His name is Alastair Guthrie; he was classics master years ago and although nearly eighty, is still as sharp as a needle.'

'What about a photograph?'

'That should be in Cassidy's file, too, although it's many years out of date.'

★ ★ ★

'Mr Guthrie?'

The short rotund man, who was almost completely bald apart from a rim of snow-white hair at the back of his head and who had been hurrying along the corridor carrying a pile of books, turned abruptly, almost dropping the whole lot.

'Yes,' he said, peering at them over the top of his half-moon spectacles.

'Sorry to have startled you. My name is Sinclair, Inspector Sinclair, and this is my colleague, Inspector Sarah Prescott. We are enquiring about a Miss Pauline Cassidy, who was a housemistress here about ten years ago, and the headmaster thought you might be able to help us. Mr Barclay did try to contact her through her mother, but that was a long time ago and he no longer has the woman's address.'

'I'll do what I can for you, but I wouldn't be too optimistic. My sanctuary is just round that corner.'

'May I carry those books for you?' asked Sinclair.

'Indeed you may. Opening the door with this load on board is a question of hope rather than expectation. Follow me and you, too, my dear.'

The two detectives accepted the offer of seats in front of the large desk, on which was a laptop, a printer and a card index box. Sinclair also noted with quiet amusement the large Toby jug full of pens, pencils, elastic bands and paper clips.

'As you see,' the man said, 'I have not become entirely submerged by modern technology, but I am up to the neck in it. You see, as public schools go, this is not a particularly large one — it has roughly four hundred pupils at any one time and on average each one stays for about four years, although a few stay on for a fifth. It was founded in 1844 and right from the start, the names of all the boys with their date of birth and the forms they were in were recorded each term in a small book, copies of which were handed out to all the pupils and we have a copy of every single one of them. So, in the hundred and sixty-four years of its existence some sixteen thousand pupils have passed through these portals, mostly boys of course, but girls in the last twenty years or so. With access to various censuses, copies of *Who's Who*, services records and so on, it has proved possible to see what happened to a substantial number of them after they left here.'

'Fascinating, and presumably pressure on a few keys on your computer will no doubt bring some of their records up?' asked Sarah.

'That's right. There's still a very long way to go, but I'm making steady progress. This job, you know, has been a lifeline for me. I'm ashamed to confess that when my Celia died, I pretty well gave up and had it not been for Barclay thinking that I needed some useful employment, I would probably have sunk into the 'Slough of Despond'.'

'Are you an old boy of the college yourself?'

'No, but I did teach classics here for many years and I'm very fond of the place. Now tell me whom you're interested in.'

'I'll leave that to my colleague and I'll take some notes,' said Sinclair.

'Do that by all means, my dear fellow, but I'll print out the entries as we go along if you like.'

'Excellent. I may just need to expand them a little as well.'

'Now, my dear, where shall I start?'

'Our main interest is in one of the mistresses, one Pauline Cassidy. She left here roughly ten years ago,' Sarah told him.

'Let's see now. Should be quite simple. The staff are all in a different section.' He operated the keys rapidly and then nodded his head. 'Yes, here we are. Pauline, Margaret Cassidy. Date of birth 28 March 1961. Educated at Feldbrook Comprehensive and Bristol University. BA Hons upper second in chemistry 1982, College of Education, chemistry teacher at Stanscombe Comprehensive School. Appointed to chemistry department here in 1988 and became housemistress of Caulfield 1992. Resigned 1998. There are no further details after that. Her next of kin recorded at that time was a Mrs Enid Cassidy, presumably her mother. There is an address here in Newbury with a phone number. There is also a colour photograph of her. It should reproduce well enough should you want a copy. Why not have a look at the screen first?'

The head and shoulders view showed an unsmiling young woman with fair hair, cut brutally short, ears that were sticking out and with her lips pressed tightly together.

'Yes, a copy would be most useful to us.'

'Anyone else?' the man asked when he had operated the printer.

'If it's not too much trouble, we would like details of twins, Adam and Kate Farrant.'

'Ah, there's a name I know well. Their father, Richard Farrant, was one of our most active old boys, right up until his tragic early death.'

'Yes, we know about that.'

'It was he who was responsible for my appointment of archivist. He helped to raise funds for the archives project and a room was set aside for a museum of old artefacts and photographs. It is just along the corridor and is coming along steadily.'

The entries of the twins didn't add to the knowledge they already had of them apart from the photographs. As an eighteen-year-old, Kate was instantly recognizable, but they looked with particular interest at the picture of Adam Farrant. Like his father, he was extremely good-looking, but without his father's open and lively facial expression. He gave the impression of being arrogant and was looking at the camera with the suspicion of a sneer on his face.

'I'm afraid that I can't give you the reason why, but we are interested in the crossed canes that used to be in the college prefects' room. Do you know if they're still there?' asked Sarah.

'No, they're in our museum now. Mr Barclay thought that that was a more suitable place for them, once it had been set up. He wanted them preserved, but decided that they ought to be moved; I gather there was some pressure from the head girl at that time, who thought that they were inappropriate considering that the college had a more enlightened view of how to discipline pupils, not to mention the fact that the practice had been degrading and typical of male insensitivity.' The man smiled at them. 'According to Mr Barclay the young lady became positively aerated. She sounded to me like a pompous, self-important harridan in the making, but obviously Barclay felt it wise to be diplomatic, but at least he refused to accede to her request that they be destroyed. Would you like to take a look at them?'

'Yes, we would,' said Sarah.

'When was corporal punishment abolished here?' asked Sinclair.

'I'm sure I could find out for you; the

164

decision would have been taken by the college council. Just a moment. Yes, here we are,' he said when he had operated the keyboard briefly. 'The decision to abolish the use of caning by the prefects was taken in the summer of 1942 and took effect from the following winter term. Caning by housemasters continued until the advent of girls here, who were admitted for the first time in the late eighties and you must know that the practice is now illegal under any circumstances — more's the pity, in my view.'

'Why so?' Sarah asked.

'Discipline is not what it was in all strata of society either at home or in schools. There is much less respect for authority and the view that it brutalized boys is not borne out by the fact that teenage behaviour of both sexes is much more violent than it was even twenty years ago. Yes, I am well aware that there are plenty of other factors that have contributed to it, but I am convinced that it played a part.

'It is often said that other societies managed perfectly well without it, such as France and Germany, but it was the war that changed things there. I'm sure you know, too, that punishments of that nature in Eire, for both boys and girls, continued long after they had been abandoned here, notably by nuns as far as the latter were concerned.' The man smiled. 'Enough of this reactionary twaddle, why don't we go along to the museum?'

The two crossed crook-handled canes were hanging on one of the walls and the man gave them a smile. 'Why not reach up, take them down and give them a swish? A lot of the old boys who come back for Founder's Day, like doing that — brings back memories, they tell me.'

Sinclair took hold of one of the canes, gave Sarah a look, raised his eyebrows slightly, and then brought it whistling down.

'I don't suppose anyone on the receiving end of one of those would forget it in a hurry.'

The man smiled. 'I remember my own experience at another school only too vividly, but despite what people say I don't think it resulted in any lasting harm.'

'I wouldn't be so sure,' said Sarah, 'but I suppose it depended on why it was done and who did it.'

The man nodded. 'I think you have something there. I always thought that a master wielding it in proportion to the offence was one thing, but boy on boy was rather different.'

★ ★ ★

'There's something worrying you about Kate Farrant's role in all this, isn't there?' Sinclair asked Sarah when they were back in the car.

'Yes, there is. Did you see Barclay's reaction when I hinted that I had some reservations about her? From all we have heard so far, I think it more than likely that Kate Farrant was gay; the security man at the club obviously thought so, Mrs Grant also hinted at it and was the woman having a liaison with Pauline Cassidy as well at the college? Their relationship there sounds to have been more than a bit close and did Barclay wonder about that, too? Did you see how unsettled he was when I hinted that I was uneasy about Kate?

'I think it quite possible that Kate fancied Rachel Lewis, but that almost certainly fell short of a physical relationship, which I feel quite sure that the girl would have rejected out of hand, as she was obviously besotted by that boy with whom she had just had her first full heterosexual experience. I doubt if the same was true with regard to Pauline Cassidy, with whom I guess she had a more intimate and long-lasting affair. If that was the case, she would have been outraged when she discovered that tape, and it also gave her the opportunity to get her revenge on the woman. I can also imagine her outrage at

167

what her brother had done to Rachel Lewis
and the opportunity to kill two birds with one
stone must have been gratifying in the
extreme.'

'What you say makes a lot of sense.'
Sinclair glanced at his watch. 'Why don't we
take the opportunity to see Mrs Cassidy?
Newbury isn't all that far away, provided, of
course, that she's still there.'

'Good idea. I'll give her a ring on my
mobile.'

7

Mrs Cassidy looked to be in her late sixties and was a thin, rather faded-looking woman who greeted them with a nervous smile.

'We're so sorry to have to descend on you at such short notice,' Sarah said after they had introduced themselves, 'but we're investigating the death of a young woman in London, who was head girl of one of the boarding houses at Brantley College when your daughter was the housemistress. I'm afraid to have to tell you that her death has occurred under very suspicious circumstances and it is important that we find out as much as we can about her. Her close family are all dead and that's why we went to the college this afternoon and they told us that she and your daughter knew each other well and had great respect for each other. The only address they have for her was yours and we wondered if you could tell us where she is now.'

A tear formed in the corner of the woman's eye and she flicked it away with her finger. 'I'm sorry. You see, I haven't seen her since she left the college. She didn't even tell me that she had decided to go and I only found out when the secretary rang to ask me what they should do with some of the things she left behind. I did get on to the headmistress, but all she said was that she was as puzzled as I obviously was. Pauline hadn't complained of being ill, or unhappy, and all Miss Sandon was able to tell me was that Pauline had said that she was so sorry to have to let them down, but for personal reasons she had to leave at once.'

'What a dreadful situation for you. Did you have anyone to whom you could turn?'

'No, there was no one I felt I could confide in and there still isn't. It would be a tremendous relief for me to talk to someone like you, who might be able to tell me if there is anything I should have done about her and if there is anything even now. Would you both like a cup of tea? I need a few moments to get my thoughts in order. After a year or so, I somehow knew that she wasn't going to come back and I tried to put it all behind me, but it didn't work and I still have nightmares about it.'

'Of course. We'd both enjoy a cup of tea. May I help you?' asked Sarah.

'No, it's all right, thank you, dear. I won't be long.'

When Enid Bishop married Frank Cassidy, their dearest wish was to have a large family.

Getting pregnant, however, proved to be difficult for her and the birth of their first child wasn't until six years after the wedding. Despite getting the best advice, which was really more than they could afford, Enid failed to conceive again and just when they were thinking that the only solution would be to adopt, Frank was found to have Hodgkin's disease and died in his late thirties. Even that would have been bearable had it not become obvious by the time that her daughter, Pauline, was in her teens, that marriage and a family were not on her agenda.

Enid Cassidy's only and much wanted child, on whom she had placed so many hopes and wishes, had proved, in the long term, a grievous disappointment to her. At first, she was everything she could have asked for, being quiet, even-tempered and industrious. Even the fact that she proved to be more than that, getting a scholarship to university from her grammar school, didn't make up for her social inadequacies. She had few friends, none close, and her total lack of interest in boys was becoming a concern for her mother. It wasn't only that; her daughter actively disliked them and was forever saying how stupid they were, seemingly thinking about almost nothing but football and boasting about their real or imagined conquests of the air-headed girls, who thought they were wonderful.

She was so pleased when Pauline, who after getting a good degree at university and was at a college of education, asked if she could bring a friend she had made there down for a few days during the summer vacation. At least, Enid Cassidy thought, if nothing else, it showed that her daughter was developing a social life at long last.

Although the friend, a very forthright woman, who was obviously a lot older than Pauline, was pleasant enough to her, it distressed her greatly to see how much her daughter seemed to be under her thumb. When, after breakfast the morning after their arrival, Pauline said that it might be nice to look round a National Trust property, her suggestion was met with scorn.

'Look how pasty you are, Pauline. What you need is fresh air and exercise to put a bit of colour into those pallid cheeks of yours. I've got a book of country walks in the car and one of those should do the trick. Got a pair of stout boots? Silly question, of course you haven't. In that case we'll have to remedy it, won't we? There must be a suitable shop near here and while we're getting them, I'm sure your mother would fix us up with a packed lunch.'

If she had had any real guts, Enid Cassidy was to think later, she would have told the woman to get it herself or go to a pub, but she had always shied away from confrontation and meekly agreed, comforting herself with the thought that a day out in the country would be good for her daughter. She was in for a shock, though. When the two young women came back, Pauline was hobbling like an old woman.

'Not to worry, Mrs Cassidy,' the friend said briskly, 'nothing wrong with her that a hot bath and a massage won't put to rights.'

From the noises coming from upstairs, it sounded as if Pauline was being put through all the tortures of the inquisition, but just how naive she had been only became apparent the following morning. When it was nearly nine o'clock and she had heard no sounds from above, she went up the stairs. Her house had three bedrooms, the big one in the front, which she occupied, and the other two at the back along the corridor past the bathroom. The door of her guest's room was shut, but that of her daughter's was open a crack. She gave it a gentle push and felt a tight constriction in her chest at the sight of the two heads side by side on the pillow.

It wasn't just that she disapproved of same-sex relationships. However much she

173

read in the women's magazines she liked to take that they were just part of the range of normal sexual behaviour, such things were against her moral and religious beliefs. They were sinful and that was all there was to it. It was also the knowledge that if Pauline was really like that, her own hopes of grandchildren were dashed for ever.

Perhaps, she was to think later, if she had taken the time to try to come to terms with it, or get advice, things might have been different, but she didn't. When the woman went out to the chemist to get some plasters for Pauline's blisters, she tackled Pauline there and then. She told her that what she was doing was sinful and wrong, but if she gave the woman up and went for counselling, she was sure that she would get over her infatuation and all would be well. It didn't work. Her daughter was very rude, said that it was her life to lead as she herself thought fit and that it was none of her mother's business. The two of them went off within minutes of the woman coming back and after that, she saw less and less of her daughter, and then came the message from the college.

'Do you recall that other woman's name?'

'I suppose I must have heard it when we were first introduced, but all I can remember now is her first name, which was Ronnie. I suppose it might have been short for Veronica, but all that stuck in my mind after they had left was that the final insult had been for her to use a man's name.' The woman shook her head and wiped away a tear with her handkerchief.

'Did she ever bring any other friends back here?'

'No and I suppose that was my fault. I still keep thinking that if I had been more open-minded, none of this might have happened.'

'Did Pauline have any money apart from what she earned?'

'Yes, she did. You see, my brother was much older than me and when he was diagnosed with inoperable lung cancer, he spoke to Frank and me about his will. He had never married and told us that he owned his house and also had some money put by and wanted to leave it to us as a family. He discussed it with me and Frank and we decided that it would allow us to get rid of the mortgage and still leave about twenty thousand pounds, which we decided that Pauline should have when she was twenty-one. At that time she was only ten and it was a tidy sum in those days, so we all agreed that it should be invested for her in trust until she was twenty-one. It meant that she was not in debt when she left college and she also had a private income after that. I don't know how much of it was left when we lost touch with one another, but she was always careful with money and with that and her teacher's salary she must have been quite well off. She certainly had a nice car and went on holidays abroad.'

'You've been able to manage all right yourself, have you?' Sarah asked.

'Yes, thank you. I do make some money doing needlework, alterations mainly, and with that, my pension and what Frank left me, I'm all right. The fact that I own the house outright, as I just explained, is also a great help.'

'I'm so glad. Would you mind if we have a quick look at your daughter's room? You see, if there is something belonging to her there, a DNA sample might be of help in tracing her.'

Out of sight of the woman, Sinclair raised his eyebrows and Sarah shook her head almost imperceptibly.

'No, of course not, but you won't find much there,' the woman said. 'You see, after a couple of years had gone by without my hearing a word from her, I decided to get rid of most of what was there. It wasn't as if there was all that much, only a few items of clothing and . . . '

'And?' enquired Sinclair.

'There was a magazine . . . '

The woman put her head in her hands and began to weep. Sarah moved quickly and put her arms round her shoulders. It took many minutes and a fresh cup of tea, but in the end she told them that she had discovered it hidden under the carpet when she had decided to let the room out to a student. It was when she had cleared it of furniture to give it a thorough clean that she had noticed that some of the tacks were missing in one corner and the carpet was loose. That was when she found the magazine. There were pictures of girls, some very young, and having things done to them that she couldn't bring herself to describe.

'What did you do with it?'

'I burnt it, of course.'

Sinclair was near certain that they wouldn't find anything of use up in the bedroom and said as much to Sarah as they went up the stairs.

'I agree, but we should at least try to get hold of some of her DNA just in case it's on the database. I know it's wildly unlikely, but I think it's something we ought to do and why do you suppose she gave her mother as next of kin when it sounds as if she split from her family completely long before she went to the

Brantley College?'

'It may not mean anything. We live in a world of forms and e-mails and perhaps the information just got into the system and was repeated after her every move.'

Sarah nodded. 'Yes, you may well be right.'

As Sinclair had expected, they found nothing of interest up there in the bedroom. It was sparsely furnished and the chest of drawers and wardrobe merely contained spare sheets and pillow cases and some clothes, which looked as if they belonged to Mrs Cassidy.

Back down in the hall, Sarah tore a sheet out of her notebook and wrote down her name and a telephone number on it.

'The extension is for my secretary,' she said, 'and I'd like you to give her a ring if Pauline contacts you, or you think of anything else that might help us to find her, in particular any object that belonged to her.'

'I'm afraid I don't hold out much hope. I have already been through all the stuff in the attic. I know a mother isn't supposed to feel like that, but she turned out to be such a disappointment to me that I couldn't bear to have any reminders of her.'

'I do understand. It must have been a very hard time for you.'

Back in the car, Sinclair looked at Sarah

and raised his eyebrows slightly. 'I know that expression on your face. You're up to something, aren't you?'

'Just a wild idea and there's almost certainly nothing to it. I feel really sorry for that woman. She obviously had great hopes for Pauline and for her to disappear completely from her life must have been very hard for her to bear.'

'Yes,' Sinclair replied, 'but I can't help thinking that it would have been even worse if she knew all about what her precious daughter had been up to.'

* ★ *

On their return to the flat that evening, they found a message from Sinclair's uncle on the answer machine, asking him to ring him back.

'I do have a little more information for you,' he said when Sinclair had got through to him, 'but unfortunately not all that much. I managed to track down a Major Thompson, who was at Sandhurst with Farrant. He clearly didn't like him; he said that he was just the sort to have won the Queen's Medal, always managing to be in the forefront of everything and being a gifted games player hadn't done him any harm, either. Most of the other cadets didn't like him at all and were delighted that he didn't get the Sword of Honour. They thought that he was just too pleased with himself and subtly sucking up to the staff. Anyway, their paths crossed again in Iraq, with Farrant in the SAS and Thompson being with an infantry regiment.

'Farrant had learned some Arabic before going out there and, as a joke, had dressed up as a native and persuaded one of his mates to bring him in, claiming that he had caught him carrying a bomb. Evidently it was some time before the others twigged and the colonel told him that if he ever did anything like that again, it would be a court martial. I gathered that it was a bit of an empty threat. Farrant was rumoured to have been involved in the rescue of some hostages and had been working undercover and as the SAS were a bit of a law unto themselves, nothing came of that escapade.

'There had been rumours for some time that there had been instances of prisoners, some of whom were later to have been shown to be completely innocent of any terrorist activity, having been beaten and humiliated and Farrant was very much in the frame, so much so that there was more serious talk of a court martial. Soon after, the man disappeared and nothing had been heard of him since. It was assumed that some of the local law lords had decided to eliminate him.'

'Did the major think that there was any possibility that he might have deserted and come back to this country?' asked Sinclair.

'He didn't deny that a man like him would have been quite capable of achieving it, but thought it highly unlikely that that had been the case and he had heard no rumours to that effect. The other man I have been able to contact is an ex sergeant of the SAS, who was involved with Farrant in some way or other. He wouldn't explain on the phone, but he was interested to hear that you were involved in an enquiry involving the man and is keen to talk to you about him.'

'You said ex. Does that mean that he has left the army altogether?'

'Yes, I gathered so. I know no more about it than that, but I do have his address, which is just over the border in Wales, and his telephone number.'

'That's very helpful and I think it would be worth going up there and having a word with him.'

'You'll let me know when you get to the bottom of all this, I hope?'

'I certainly will, but at the moment it's more a question of if rather than when. Many thanks for all the trouble you've taken.'

'Any time. You only have to ask.'

Once he had crossed the older of the two bridges across the Severn and driven through Chepstow past the racecourse, Sinclair really enjoyed the rest of the drive along the Wye.

'What an amazing view,' he said, after he had introduced himself to the ex sergeant and was looking back at Tintern Abbey, across the river from where they were standing at the door of the cottage perched on the side of the hill.

'Yes. I come from these parts. I was born in Chepstow and my dad worked on the racecourse. I even had ambitions to be a jump jockey when I was a lad, but you can see why that didn't work out.'

Sinclair could. Ron Cross was a good three inches over his own six feet two and powerfully built with it.

'You want to know about Farrant?'

'Yes, his twin sister has been murdered. It seems that the two of them didn't get on and we are trying to find out as much about the family as possible. We know that he disappeared while serving in Iraq and any information about that might be very useful.'

'And you're wondering if he could have got back to this country?'

'Yes. It's a possibility we're considering and

we'd like to get a clearer idea of what sort of a man he is. I've already made some enquiries about him with the military authorities but got almost nowhere.'

'I can't say that surprises me. I've had contact with the man on a number of occasions in the last few years, first in Northern Ireland and then in Iraq. You may or may not know that the other ranks have a say as to whether an officer gets into the SAS or not. I was against it, but the others didn't agree. They thought he was as tough as any of them, brave and with no side to him — one of the boys, in fact. What they didn't seem to see was that he was a cruel bastard. He was smart enough not to be caught doing any of the things he was rumoured to be involved in, but all that changed in Iraq.

'I was in charge of a patrol on the outskirts of Basra, when I heard strange sounds coming from the basement of a building that had all but been destroyed by a suicide bomber. There was a sharp series of cracks, followed by a high-pitched keening sound. One didn't fool around with strange noises in Basra at that time, I can tell you — we knew more than enough about booby traps — but I decided to go in. I won't bore you with the precautions I took but I burst into that cellar, my automatic assault rifle at the ready.

'I shall never forget the scene down there. A young girl, a fourteen- or maybe a fifteen-year-old, was lying on her back on a low table. Her wrists were tied together and were being held stretched out behind her head by an Arab man, probably no more than three or four years older than her. Her ankles were also tied down to the table, her feet protruding some six inches below its end. In the seconds before I bellowed at them to freeze, another man in Arab dress brought the thin cane he was holding flashing down and it landed with a sharp crack on the soles of her bare feet. As the girl went into a spasm of agony, her body arching off the table, I near as anything shot the bastard dead. As you probably have guessed already, it was Farrant.

'Of course he was full of almost plausible reasons why he was there and had been forced into beating the girl. He had, he told me, been working undercover, he had made contact with the family, several members of which were in that cellar and they had vital intelligence to impart. Before they did so, though, and in order to test his trustworthiness to the full, he was to be the instrument of punishment of the youngest daughter of the family who had refused her father's order to marry an influential man, who was prepared to overlook some slight he harboured against them, provided the girl became his bride.

"What you have to understand,' Farrant said, when an enquiry was set up, 'is that to be trusted and become one of these people, you have to accept certain aspects of their culture and way of doing things that may be abhorrent to one. If it hadn't been me, it would have been one of her brothers and the punishment would have been even harsher."

'And did the authorities buy that?' asked Sinclair.

'I'm not sure, but I certainly didn't. You should have seen the expression on the bastard's face seconds after he had hit that girl. He may have been wearing loose clothing, but there was no hiding his arousal.

'If I had been called to give evidence at the enquiry, I would not have held back either about what I had seen, or what I thought of the filthy swine, but it never got as far as that. He was held in such loose confinement after the enquiry had dragged on to another day, that even my old dad could have got away and so he escaped and that was it.

'I was so disillusioned both by that and other things that were going on that I decided to pack it in and I haven't regretted that for an instant.'

185

'Have you any idea what happened to the girl?'

'No. The last thing the powers-that-be wanted was to get involved in local politics of that sort and once Farrant was out of the way, the matter was dropped. I shall never forget that poor girl, though. And I have often wondered what became of her.'

'Do you think that a man like Farrant would have been able to make it back to this country after he escaped?'

'I have no doubt about that. He was dark complexioned, knew more about the Arab culture than any of us and although he didn't speak the language all that well, he could get by in it. I talked to a number of moderate Arabs about that series of events and they thought that the family of the girl might even have helped Farrant to get away.'

'Really?'

'Yes. You see, they have an entirely different view of many things compared to the likes of us. In their eyes, that girl had let down the honour of her family by disobeying her father and deserved the punishment being given. Apparently her brother would have been only too happy to carry it out himself. No doubt, too, they were using Farrant in some way or other.'

'How do you suppose Farrant managed to

get into that position with the family?'

'I don't know. Weapons, money, information are all things he might have been able to get hold of. Do you think he's over here, yourself?'

'It's a possibility, but there are some aspects of what has gone on that don't fit with what I've heard about the man and thanks to you I've got a much better feel of him.'

'If he's not dead already, I only hope that you catch the bastard.'

After lunch, they went for a walk along the banks of the Wye.

'What are you planning to do now?' Sinclair asked.

'I'm negotiating with some sponsors to start courses on canoeing, climbing, abseiling and trekking in the region around here.'

'What an excellent plan and very rewarding, I have no doubt. I did some of the Duke of Edinburgh awards years ago and I look back on them with enormous pleasure and a sense of achievement. Good luck to you.'

'And to you. If that bastard did get back here, nail him for me.'

★ ★ ★

By the time Sinclair was approaching the turn-off to Slough on the M4, it was almost six o'clock and the traffic was almost at a standstill. It was clearly only going to get worse and remembering that the Farrants' old house had been near Beaconsfield, he decided to turn off and take a look at it. When he reckoned that he was roughly in the right area, he pulled into the car park of a pub, went in and ordered a cappuccino.

'I'm looking for Streatfield Manor,' he said, showing his warrant card to the landlord who was standing near the bar. 'It used to belong to a family called Farrant and I believe it's somewhere quite close to here.'

'It's a country house hotel now,' the man said, 'and it's about half a mile up the road from here. Pretty popular it is, too. You see, it's within easy range of the airport and not so close that the aircraft noise is a major issue. It's got great facilities, too, with a swimming pool, fitness centre, tennis courts and impressive grounds. There are also stables quite near where the guests can go riding and it has an arrangement with a nearby golf course. As a result it's also popular for weekend breaks.'

'A place like that must take a lot of your custom away.'

'No, the very reverse, in fact. My predecessor thought it would and I got it on the cheap, but once all the building work up there was finished and the heavy lorries had departed, business here began to pick up and now we're doing quite well. You see, in addition to people staying for some time, there are others who are there just for one night before flying off. They get a package of bed and breakfast, free parking and transport to and from the airport. What they don't want is an expensive slap-up dinner and so they take a country walk, find this place, have a drink or two and then something more modest to eat.'

'Did you know the Farrants, the people who were here before it was a hotel?'

The man shook his head. 'No, that was long before my time.'

'What about locals? Do you know anyone who's been living here a long time?'

'Not that many. I reckon the best person for you to try would be Meg Drake. She lives in a cottage that used to be part of the estate and was used by her dad, the head gardener. It's no great distance straight up the road from here. It's just short of the main gates to the hotel and if you reach them, you've gone too far.'

'Thanks, she sounds just the sort of person I'm after.'

Meg Drake was an attractive-looking woman, who must, Sinclair thought, have been in her middle forties.

'Let me get you a drink,' she said, when he had explained that he was looking into the death of Kate Farrant.

'Thanks,' he said, 'just a plain tonic water for me, if you've got it, or some other soft drink.'

The woman smiled, nodded and went to the cabinet on the opposite side of the room. 'I think I can run to that.' When she had poured it out and a glass of sherry for herself, she motioned him to sit down and did so herself on the other side of the fireplace. 'Yes,' she said, 'I saw it in the paper. All it said was that she'd died after a short illness. Dreadful thing to happen and, let me see, she can only have been about thirty. I also saw some time ago that Adam had gone missing in Iraq; it's almost as if the family was cursed in some way. At least, that's the way my mother would have put it. She was a great one for astrology and fortune telling. How did you find out about me?'

'The chap who runs the pub down the road told me that your father used to be the head gardener of the estate and I've also spoken to the headmaster of Brantley College, who was a friend of Richard Farrant and came here for his wedding reception.'

The woman nodded. 'The Farrant family

as a whole shaped my life to an extraordinary degree and if it hadn't been for them things would have been very different for me.'

★ ★ ★

Meg Drake's father was a dour and obsessional man, rigid and joyless and hard-working. The church and the subservient place of women in the scheme of things were what he believed in and practised. It wasn't that he was violent or a bully, he was just deadly dull and had little to say other than about the garden and its contents. Despite that, it wasn't a bad life for his wife; they lived in the lodge of the big house rent free, she had friends amongst the other staff there and in the village and she lavished all the love she didn't get from her husband, on Meg, their only child. She also enjoyed sewing and knitting and was a key figure in the group of women who were doing the tapestry on the kneelers that were to replace the old ones in the church. Meg, though, was her real delight. She was lively, pretty and when she started at primary school, it was obvious that she was bright as well.

Meg remembered with absolute clarity the event that changed her life for ever, not least because she had relived it so many times. Mr

Farrant from the big house always used to wave to her and would occasionally give her an apple or a sweet when he was passing and saw her in the garden of the lodge. She was a friendly, outgoing six-year-old at the time and always had a smile for him and that morning was taking down the washing from the line, standing on a chair, when it happened.

'Hello, young Meg. Come and see our two new Beagle puppies.'

Leaning over the fence was the beaming face of Mr Farrant from the big house. She just knew that her mother wouldn't let her, but how wrong she was.

'Where are you, Mrs D?' he bellowed and when she appeared at the back door, smiled and waved his stick at her. 'I'm just going to take Meg to see the new puppies. Won't be long.'

The woman smiled back. 'Not too many sweets, mind, and be sure to bring her back in good time for lunch.'

'Fear not, Mrs D, your wish is my command.'

He reached over the fence, lifted her up and hoisted her on to his shoulders and off they went. That was the start of it. Fred Drake didn't really approve — he was a great believer in people knowing their place in the scheme of things — but if Mr Farrant wanted to take an interest in the small girl, that was his prerogative. After all, he was both the owner of the property and his employer. Having an extremely limited vocabulary, though, he wouldn't have known what a word like prerogative meant, let alone used it. He also knew perfectly well, even though the man was always friendly and good-tempered, that his job and the cottage were at stake should he upset Mr Farrant.

After that, the world changed completely for young Meg. She had the run of the grounds, she learned to ride on one of the ponies, and Mrs Farrant, who was a lovely lady, much older than her husband, taught her how to speak properly, encouraged her with her school work, played simple card games with her and, more than that, provided the cuddles and fun that were all too rare at home. Her father considered that life was a serious business and strongly discouraged his wife from showing her too much affection and levity. And then there was the Farrants' son, Richard. He was about fifteen then and Meg thought he was wonderful. Over the next few years, during his holidays from boarding school, they fooled about in the swimming pool, he taught her how to swim properly, and even to play tennis passably well.

She was fifteen when Richard announced

he was getting married and when he asked her to be one of his bridesmaids, she knew that her father would never agree to it.

'Nonsense, Fred,' Mr Farrant Senior said in his booming voice. 'You're all part of the family and we expect you and Doris to be there and don't tell me that you're going to deny Richard the pleasure of having Meg join the other bridesmaids. If you're worried about dressing up, your Sunday best will be more than enough and there'll be plenty of others the same. And no one is going to force a drink on you — I know and respect your views on that. Some of your excellent elderflower cordial will be available for you and others of the same persuasion. Fancy wedding suits for men are quite ridiculous and I wouldn't wear one myself if I had a choice, but you know what women are like and they must have their way.'

'But what about Meg?'

'That's all taken care of. All the bridesmaids will be dressed alike and, before you ask, I'm looking after that, for all four of 'em. You don't need me to tell you that she's as pretty as a picture and, believe you me, she'll outshine the others.' He gave the man a beaming smile. 'Thanks to you, the garden and the grounds are an absolute picture and we couldn't possibly have the proudest day of my life spoiled by not having the architect there, could we? Cheer up, Mr D, you'll have the time of your life.'

Her parents did come and they did enjoy it, even though her father wouldn't admit it, and the other bridesmaids made Meg more than welcome. Had Mrs Farrant, or even Richard, had a word with them beforehand, she wouldn't have put it past them. She had never been so happy. With the others she was given a really beautiful handbag as a present and even got a hug and a kiss from the best man. A year later, she was just about to leave school with the dreary prospect of some boring dead-end job, when, directly after the twins were born, Annabel had the breakdown that resulted in her suicide and she was asked if she'd help Richard's mother with the children. She jumped at the chance, not least because it would mean she would have to move into the big house and get away from her grumpy and taciturn father.

It was made as easy as possible for her. It was hard work and she had very little time off, but Mrs Farrant Senior, despite her severe arthritis, was always there to help and instruct, all the laundry was taken care of, everyone was friendly and she was made to feel part of the family. Richard was also there a lot of the time and was a hands-on father and made sure that she got some free time and exercise with riding and swimming.

She genuinely loved the children until they were five or six, but then began to dislike and finally hate them. By the age of eleven they were at separate boarding schools, which gave her a rest from them during term time and she was able to help old Mr Farrant with some secretarial work. During one of the summer terms he arranged for her to have shorthand and typing lessons and she also picked up enough computer skills to be able to handle his correspondence and use the internet and e-mails.

By this time, Adam had become a bully and a liar and was showing the signs of the testosterone-driven menace which was only to get worse as he got older, while Kate began to terrify Meg. The girl was now a joyless workaholic, whose weapon against Adam was subtle terror. Meg remembered him saying to Kate after some verbal put-down that one of these days he was going to beat the daylights out of her. Her reply? It was to stare at him with those cold dark eyes of hers and say, 'That's nothing compared to what I'll do to you if you even attempt it.' 'Ha!' he replied. 'I'm twice as strong as you.' 'Yes,' she said, 'but like everyone else, you have to sleep, don't you?' After that, he always locked his bedroom door, not only during the night but during the day as well.

The last straw for Meg was two years later. From her bedroom window, she saw the two of them fooling about in the pool. Adam tried to duck his sister, but she slipped out of his grasp and made for the ladder at the shallow end. He caught her when she was halfway up and yanked her bikini bottoms down to her knees. Meg could see him laughing as he reached up towards her as she turned round, but then he fell back as her headbutt took him full on the nose and he disappeared under the water, a crimson stain spreading upwards. By the time he managed to get out of the water, his left hand cupped over his face, Kate had long since disappeared.

Meg had had enough. That incident wasn't the only thing that worried her. She had caught him photographing her when she was sunbathing by the pool and he had developed a way of looking at her that made it only too clear what he would like to do.

★   ★   ★

'So how did you cope with that?' Sinclair asked.

'I plucked up courage and went to see Richard, telling him what had happened and that I couldn't stand it any longer.'

'And his reaction?'

'He told me how sorry he was for having given me so little thought over the preceding few months. It was no excuse, he realized, but with his father's death and his mother in a nursing home, he had been blind to the behaviour of the children and of course I must leave. Anyway, the big house was going to be sold and he had already had approaches from a consortium with plans to turn it into a country house hotel. As to the lodge, part of the deal was for him to retain it with a bit more land than it had already and my mother and I would be able to stay there rent free for as long as we wished — my father had died two years earlier. As to the immediate future, he asked me if I would consider staying until the start of the twins' new term — they were both about to go to a mixed private boarding school — and then he would like to give me a week's holiday in London.

'It was pathetic, really. I had fantasies of staying with him in the Savoy with a double bedroom overlooking the Thames and making passionate love with him in the moonlight! In the event, I had my own very comfortable bedroom in Richard's flat in the club he owned in South Kensington. Yes, I did leave the door unlocked, but I slept undisturbed!

Still, I had an amazing time. He took me to many of the things I had heard about: a ride on the London Eye, a river trip to the Tower, a musical and yes, dinner at the Savoy with a decorous dance afterwards. No, I wasn't ravished in a four-poster, I didn't even get a kiss, but he made sure that I didn't see the children again.'

'What happened then?' Sinclair asked.

'I did a proper secretarial course and got a job with GlaxoSmithKline, which is not that far away, helped I'm sure by a glowing reference from Richard, and I'm still there.'

'And your mother?'

'She developed cancer some ten years ago and when she was dying, she told me something that explained so much. It might have come out of one of the Victorian novels written by women that Mrs Farrant gave me to read and I wouldn't be surprised to discover that she had known what had happened all along. After all, she was pretty crippled with her rheumatoid arthritis and maybe she thought that if she wasn't able to give her husband what he so clearly needed, why shouldn't someone else provide it. They still loved each other, didn't they, and that was all that mattered. I'm sure in your job you must come across all sorts of strange domestic arrangements and perhaps you won't be surprised to hear my father wasn't an ill-educated and dour gardener, he was Mr Farrant Senior.

'He would have arranged for a termination directly she told him that she was pregnant if that was what she wanted, but my mother wouldn't hear of it and finally agreed to the plan he had hatched up. Terminally ill though my mother was when she told me all this, she was still able to raise a smile when she said that the most tricky part of the whole exercise was to make her new husband believe that he was the father of the child. Of course, people with my mother's background at that time didn't talk about that sort of thing in detail, let alone with their daughter, but she made it clear enough that following their wedding and after the first few distinctly unimpressive episodes, he was only too pleased that she seemed to acknowledge that he had done his duty by her, that the desired result had been achieved and there was no need to put each other through it again. I mustn't mock him, though: the poor man, although a genius in the garden, was of very limited intelligence and clearly had been dragooned into marriage. I can just see Mr Farrant putting it to him. 'We all know what an upright churchgoing man you are, Fred, but having a wife to support you would be the icing on the cake and add to your status in the community. I happen to know that Doris, up at the house, admires you greatly. She's no flighty young girl, she's a serious-minded mature woman, and you'd be a fool to pass up the opportunity of having a wife whom everyone would think most suitable.'

'He certainly had that something, did old Mr Farrant. You may find it difficult to believe that he could pull off anything like that, but then you never met him. Did he go on seeing my mother after their wedding and I had been born? I like to think that he did. I hadn't failed to notice the way they used to smile at each other and to me, she always seemed happier than she had any right to be. After all, her husband was a good enough man in his way, but the problem was that his way most certainly wasn't hers. It was a very bizarre arrangement, but it didn't work so badly — at least that's what I think — and one can't say that about all that many more conventional marriages, at least judged by the current divorce rate.'

'That's certainly true. What happened about this cottage?'

'Richard left me the freehold in his will. I often wondered if he would have changed his mind had his life not been cut short so tragically, but I like to believe that he wouldn't have done so. I also wondered if Adam or Kate would contest it, but they didn't and I never saw either of them again. So, here I am, financially independent and I have been seeing a very charming widower, who is only a few years older than me.' She gave him a smile. 'I may have been a late starter, but let me just say that it's been well worth the wait.'

'I'm very pleased for you.'

'Thank you. Is Adam Farrant dead?'

'I think it very likely.'

'It is a dreadful thing to say, but I can't say I'm sorry. He was a truly dreadful person.'

Meg Drake watched through the window as the detective drove off. What memories his visit had brought back, not least of Richard Farrant. Was it so very wrong of her to fantasize about him at certain times when she was with her new partner friend? Maybe, she thought, but she had no intention of feeling guilty about it.

8

Sarah had arranged to meet Jack Pocock at The Spinning Wheel Club late in the morning, but decided to get there in good time and was let in by Bert Powell, the security man, who had taken to coming into work much earlier since the tragedy of Kate Farrant's death.

'Miss Corsie not in here today?'

'She's gone to have a lunchtime meeting with Sir Richard Hartley, ma'am. He's the chairman of the members committee and they're no doubt trying to decide what to do. She had a word with Mrs Grant and me before she left and explained that the club's future depended on Miss Farrant's will and whether or not she's left it to anyone.'

'So it's not a company?'

'No, it isn't. I remember overhearing Miss Farrant telling someone, I can't recall who it was, that she owned it outright.'

'Do you know where Miss Farrant was during the day before she was taken ill?'

'Well, she was certainly here when I arrived myself at about twelve, but she may have gone out through the outside door at the back of her flat. I could always check that on the security camera if you like. I switch off the ones focused on the tables after all the girls have gone each evening, but those on the front and back doors of the building are left on permanently.'

'Would you? I'm interested from the time she went down to her flat to the arrival of the ambulance men.'

'All right, ma'am. I'm afraid it's going to take some time.'

'That's no problem. I shall be in the flat for most of the afternoon.'

Jack Pocock arrived soon after midday and showed her round.

'The big problem, as I'm sure you know already,' he said, 'is that no one realized that there were any suspicious circumstances attached to the woman's death until some ten days later when Dr Tredgold established that she had been poisoned by thallium. During that time, not unreasonably, the flat had been cleaned thoroughly, the toilet disinfected and the soiled carpet and bed linen burnt. We did find some traces of thallium on the floorboards under where the carpet had been but that didn't tell us anything we didn't know already.

'Dr Tredgold thought it most likely that the thallium had been put in a drink rather than food and we took particular care over that particular aspect. It appears that Kate Farrant was a teetotaller and apart from milk and mineral water in the fridge, there was no other bottled drink in the flat. The administrator did tell us that she noticed that there were some empty bottles of her usual make of water on the bedside table when she went down to inspect the damage and these were thrown out and removed with the rest of the rubbish by the refuse collectors a couple of days later during their normal round. As to the glass, that was put through the dishwasher in the kitchen upstairs, which is used by the club.'

'Hmm. Any indication of what she might have eaten that evening?'

'You'll have to ask the woman who supervised the cleaning up — all the rubbish had been taken away by the time we arrived and the same applies to the contents of the fridge, although the contents of the freezer are still there.'

'What about the rest of the flat?'

'It's quite large and in addition to the living quarters, consisting of two bedrooms, a dining and sitting room, Miss Farrant had an office, in which were details of the club's finances, lists of members and employees and a separate filing cabinet for her own personal and financial affairs. Some of the documents are still being studied, but a preliminary look at them and interviews with her solicitor and bank manager suggest that not only was Miss Farrant an extremely wealthy woman, but the club was also prospering and all its affairs were in good order. There is still a good deal to do, but there was a remarkable lack of personal effects, such as family photographs and correspondence down there, and no evidence has been found so far that she had made a will. If she did, it is not in the flat, nor is there a copy lodged with the solicitor who deals with the affairs of the club. I suppose it's possible that she employs a different firm for her private affairs.'

'Any evidence that she had another property elsewhere?' asked Sarah.

'Not that has been discovered so far.'

'Any documents of interest?'

'There was a lot about the club, accounts, details of employees and a note of the things held in her bank, such as her birth certificate and the deeds of this building.'

'What about her personal finances?'

'Bank statements are here, correspondence with her financial adviser and so on. She was an extremely wealthy woman.'

'Any personal correspondence?'

'No, none at all. There is quite a lot of stuff to do with the charity.'

'I'd like to look at details of the staff here, please, Jack.'

There was a section devoted to that in the locked filing cabinet, the keys for which were found in her desk in the study, the door of which they had found secured with an entry pad rather than a key. The longest-serving person was Mrs Grant, now aged sixty-four; she had been in the post for nearly twenty years, having previously been matron at a private girls boarding school. Jill Corsie was forty-seven. She had had secretarial training and was first secretary, then office manager and finally personal assistant to the managing director of a firm manufacturing medical equipment, which was situated in Basingstoke. There was a copy of her application to The Spinning Wheel Club and a note from Richard Farrant to the effect that both he and the other two members of the appointment committee had found her to be easily the most impressive of the three candidates for the post of administrator of the club. The woman's reason for wanting to come to London was to be close to an aunt, her only living relative, who was partially disabled and living alone. A note in Farrant's handwriting indicated that the woman had died three years after her appointment, but that she was happy with the job and wanted to stay. After that, Farrant had written: 'Thank the Lord for that. She has proved excellent at the job, hard-working, efficient and stands no nonsense with the croupiers and also handles the members tactfully.'

'What about the doors to the front and back entrances, Jack?' Sarah asked when she had finished with the paperwork.

'The door to the outside has both a Yale type and a mortice lock on it as well as bolts on the inside. The door itself is solid oak and it's no surprise that the ambulance men couldn't make any impression on it. All the windows are fitted with bars.

'Mrs Grant the housekeeper knew the code for opening the door leading to the front hall of the club up the flight of stairs, which made our task much easier. It has a combination lock on it with a four-digit code. No one at all, apart from Mrs Grant, was allowed into the flat alone and Miss Farrant's study was only ever cleaned when she was there in person and able to supervise it.'

'Thank you, Jack, I must clearly have another word with the housekeeper.'

★ ★ ★

Sarah found Mrs Grant in her flat.

'It's nice to see you again,' she said. 'This

must be a very worrying time for you.'

'It is and sad, too, for all of us.'

Twenty minutes later, after a cup of tea and hearing about her personal anxieties about the future and those of the girls and the rest of the staff, Sarah got up to go and paused at the door.

'I wonder if I could ask you a favour?'

'Of course, dear.'

'We are working on the possibility that Miss Farrant either ate or drank something that disagreed with her violently and I wonder if you'd be good enough to show me exactly how her fridge was stocked and where the juice and mineral water came from.'

The woman nodded. 'I'd be glad to. We'd better start with the kitchen on the ground floor, where our barman Tony Adams prepares the snacks for the members and where the spare drinks, which are not kept in the bar upstairs, are stored.'

Sarah followed the woman downstairs and when they were in the kitchen pointed to the cupboard set high up on one of the walls.

'Miss Farrant was a teetotaller and I kept a supply of mineral water and grapefruit juice in that cupboard. Every morning when Miss Farrant was in residence, I took fresh rolls down to her flat at seven o'clock and checked the contents of her fridge. She liked to have a couple of cartons of grapefruit juice there and three of her special mineral water and I also made sure that there were reserves of marmalade and butter down there and enough food for her lunch and supper. I made a note of any deficiencies and replaced them when I went down later to make her bed and clean the bathroom.'

'Was she a fussy eater?'

'Not at all. She told me once that she was just like her father, who used to say 'I'm easy to please, because I don't like anything'. That's not to say that she didn't eat a balanced diet. She ate out for lunch most days and I'm sure she got fruit and vegetables then. She liked apples and bananas and I kept a fresh supply for her in the small larder down there. All I can say is that she had a very trim figure and until her last illness, she never ailed a thing.'

'Where did you do the shopping?'

'I didn't have to do any. The club has a daily delivery for the members and if I saw that Miss Farrant was in need of anything, I'd ring them and they'd add it to the list. I kept a store of the grapefruit juice and mineral water in that cupboard up there and that was off limits to the steward, not that he would ever have wanted to pirate any of Miss

Farrant's supplies. Mostly, as far as soft drinks are concerned, he stocks mineral water, still and fizzy, tonic water and orange juice. The beer, wines and spirits are kept locked up in the bar on the first floor.

'I also help Tony Capelli, the barman, in here from time to time. He brings in canapes from the local deli, which his father runs, on a daily basis and also a selection of cheeses, biscuits and so on. He arranges them down here and then serves them to the members from the bar.'

'Where did Miss Farrant's grapefruit juice and mineral water come from?'

'As far as I know, Tony got it from the local supermarket and she wasn't fussy about the make.'

'How often was she away?'

'I'd say for a night or two most weeks. She'd never tell me about that, I'd just discover that she wasn't there when I went down in the morning, but she'd always let me know if it was to be much longer. I'd say that she'd been away much more recently.'

'Did she ever have visitors to stay?'

'Never.'

'One last thing. Did you notice anything unusual about either Miss Farrant or her flat the day before she died?'

The woman thought for a moment. 'No, I

can't say that I did.'

'Have you any spare cartons of juice and bottles of mineral water still up in that cupboard? I'd like to take a couple of each away with me.'

Mrs Grant nodded. 'Would you mind lifting them down yourself? It's a bit high for me and normally I have to get up on a chair unless Tony is here.'

'I'd very much like a word with him,' Sarah said when she had put the two cartons and bottles into a paper bag. 'Would it be possible to get hold of him?'

'He helps his dad out in the delicatessen when he's not working here and it's only a few hundred yards away. He should be there now. I'll point out the way for you when you leave, if you like. I'm going up to my flat now and should you need anything else, my number's three on the internal phone — there's one over there.'

'Excellent.'

After thanking the woman and watching her climb the staircase back up to her flat, Sarah went down into the basement and found Jack Pocock still working in Kate Farrant's study.

'Do you reckon you can do that for me?' she asked when she had explained what she wanted. 'I'll wait for you in the lobby.'

The man merely nodded and started up the stairs.

'Did you get it, Jack?' she asked when he returned some ten minutes later.

The man nodded, handing her a small plastic bottle.

'Good man. Thanks for your help. I've seen all I want for the moment, but I'd like to have a word with Miss Corsie when she gets back. Any reason why they shouldn't open the club up again if that's what they want?'

'No, but this flat should remain secure for the time being.'

'Right.'

Next, Sarah found the delicatessen, which was quite close to the underground station.

Tony Capelli was a cheerful-looking young man, with black, curly hair, and gave her a cheeky grin when she introduced herself, raising his thick eyebrows.

'I'm trying to get as clear an idea as possible of the way the club operates and I'm interested in the pantry you use for preparing the food for the members. Do you keep it locked when you're upstairs in the bar?'

The young man shook his head. 'Not worth the bother. It's not as if there's anything in there worth nicking. The drinks are all in the bar upstairs except a few spares and those I do lock up in the cupboard under the worktop.

'If I don't watch out, the odd member does nip in there for a quick bite before they go upstairs and get stuck into the games.'

'Anyone in particular?'

'There's one big fat bloke who does it quite often, but I don't mind; he always slips me a couple of quid if I catch him at it.'

'Does he have glasses with a ribbon attached to the arms?'

'That's the fellow.'

★　★　★

'You've been up to something, haven't you?' Sinclair said when they were sitting over their supper in Sarah's flat. 'I know that look in your eye.'

'Let's leave it until tomorrow, shall we? I'm whacked and I also need to get my head round some of the things I've discovered today.'

'Sounds intriguing. I'll keep my powder dry, too. How about a little relaxation therapy instead to stop you adding 'night to the day's work'.'

'Not another of your dreaded quotations?'

''Fraid so. Virgil. It turned up in the crossword the other day, but I've spared you the Latin!'

214

'Thank goodness for that, but for once at least I understand it and the suggestion is both needed and would suit me admirably.'

After breakfast the following morning, when Sinclair had told her about his visits to Tintern and Buckinghamshire, Sarah went across to the fridge and took out the carton of grapefruit juice.

'What's this? Practising some new health kick, are you?'

Sarah raised her eyebrows. 'That remains to be seen. I think I have discovered how the murderer might have been able to poison Kate Farrant. You see, her somewhat eccentric and almost exclusive choices of drink were grapefruit juice and bottled water. Both were supplied as part of the regular order from the local supermarket. Some was occasionally used by members of the club and kept with the other supplies of drink, but that for Kate was kept separately in a cabinet in the pantry, from which the housekeeper replenished the fridge in her flat as required. Now, watch this.'

Picking up her handbag, Sarah took a syringe with a needle attached from its plastic holder and after turning the carton upside-down, inserted the needle under the wings beneath its cap and withdrew five millilitres of the juice. Placing the carton upright again,

215

she detached the body of the syringe, leaving the needle in place, discarding the juice in its barrel and drew up some water in place of it.

'All that remains,' she said, 'is to inject the thallium solution like this, extract the needle, plug the tiny hole with this clear sealant that Jack supplied and hey presto, the deed is done.'

She waited for a minute or so, then shook the carton vigorously. 'See, not a drop has escaped, the plug is held under the wings of the carton and in any case is virtually invisible. Take a look!'

Sinclair did so and then clapped softly. 'That's brilliant. All your idea?'

Sarah coloured slightly and nodded. 'Mrs Grant used to go down to the basement flat every morning at about ten o'clock to make the bed, change the sheets when necessary and clean the bath and shower. She also made a note of how much juice, water and other provisions needed to be replenished, such as fresh fruit and frozen meals, and went back up and down again with the supplies.

'As a result of all the mess following Kate's disastrous gastroenteritis and the major cleaning-up operation after she had been taken to hospital, it's not surprising that Jack found so little down there and the used cartons and bottles — it seems likely that she drank at least two of each — were taken away with the soiled towels and carpets and either incinerated or taken to a landfill site. As Jack said, there's no reasonable chance of their being found and it's certainly not worth the effort of instituting a search.'

'Do you think that that implies that the murderer was one of the residents or people who worked at the club?'

'Not necessarily. Any of the members could have found out that the cartons of grapefruit juice were for Kate's exclusive use, have bought an identical make and prepared the poisoned carton at their leisure, substituted it for one of the others and then waited to see what happened. We have no means of knowing how much of the juice she drank at a time and perhaps it was sheer chance that the day in question was both hot and humid and as a result she put away more than usual.'

'Did Jack have any observations to make?'

Sarah smiled. 'He merely said that he couldn't find fault with my reasoning.'

'Praise indeed. Any other rabbits due to come out of your hat?'

'Well, there is one. You see, I had another idea and I'm still waiting to hear from Tredgold about that. He promised to give me the result as soon as possible and in the meantime, this is what I suggest.'

Sinclair listened with intense concentration to what she had to say. 'It makes sense,' he said when she had finished, 'and I must say that that particular scenario hadn't occurred to me. So, in the meantime you plan to pay another visit to the club?'

'Yes, the woman Tredgold mentioned to me isn't free for the next couple of days and I would like you to come with me when she is.' Sinclair nodded. 'There is one last thing. Kate's car is still in the garage at the side of the house and Jack found the documentation for it in her desk in the study. She bought it from a main dealer in Reading — it's a Porsche Boxter S convertible — and, as it appears that she was often away for several days at a time, I was wondering if she had a place somewhere near there in addition to her flat. It's true that Jack failed to find any record of her having another house and the address on the car's paperwork is that of the club, but I thought it worth following up.'

'What brain food have you been eating? Why don't we go to Reading this morning?'

★ ★ ★

The showroom of the garage was full of gleaming cars and Sinclair raised his eyebrows as he saw the price tags on them.

'We're quite obviously in the wrong profession,' he said. 'Even though we assumed that Kate Farrant was extremely well off, paying the best part of fifty thousand for a car is pretty mind-boggling.'

'Yes,' the salesman said after he had come up to them and asked if he could help, 'I remember the lady quite clearly.' They had shown their warrant cards and explained that they were looking into the unexpected death of Kate Farrant. 'And I am very sorry to hear that she has passed away. It's not often we get a client with such definite ideas or one who acts so decisively. She wanted the new car as soon as possible, the part-exchange value she put on her current one was not negotiable, although she understood that we would need to inspect it and take it for a test drive. She was prepared to pay the difference by direct debit there and then and suggested that I consult my manager. If her terms were not acceptable, she would go somewhere else.'

Sinclair raised his eyebrows. 'That fits in with what we know about the lady and you obviously did agree to the deal.'

'Yes. Sales had been rather slack, her own car was in immaculate condition and we didn't want to lose the chance of servicing the new vehicle, either.'

'This location is not exactly convenient for

someone living in South Kensington. Did she leave an address anywhere in this neighbourhood?'

'No, she didn't, but when she brought it in for its first service, she was accompanied by another lady in a different car and left us a telephone number so that we would be able to inform her when the Boxter was ready for collection.'

'Do you still have the details in the records?'

'It'll be on our database.' He entered the details on his keyboard. 'Yes, here it is.'

After thanking the man, they returned to the car. 'In view of the fact that Kate was quite often away for several days,' Sarah said, 'it seems quite likely that she was living for at least some of the time at the place with this phone number and if she was sharing it with someone, as also appears possible, it would obviously make sense for us to pay it a visit.'

'I agree,' Sinclair replied.

Sarah keyed in the phone number into the satellite navigation system, which led them to a detached stone cottage some ten miles from the centre of Andover. It had a thatched roof, a neat garden in front and to one side, with a garage on the other and a paddock behind in which two horses were grazing.

Although she looked pale and drawn, Sarah

recognized the woman who answered their knock at once from the photograph she had obtained from the secretary at the offices of The Frampton Trust.

'Miss Fisher?'

'Yes.'

'I'm Detective Inspector Prescott and this is my colleague Inspector Sinclair. We're from the Metropolitan Police and are looking into the sad and unexpected death of Kate Farrant.'

The woman glanced at the warrant card, then looked up at them and nodded. 'You'd better come in.'

When they were seated in the living room, which had an attractive inglenook fireplace and was comfortably furnished with a settee and two armchairs, Sarah looked at the woman, who met her gaze without dropping her eyes.

'I read about Kate's death in the paper,' she said, 'and was deeply shocked and upset. I knew she was ill because she was due to come to stay here at the weekend and when she didn't turn up I rang the housekeeper at her club and the woman there told me that she had been taken ill and was in hospital.

I wasn't able to get any further information either from her or when I rang the ward sister, who merely told me that she wasn't well enough to receive visitors at present. I had never known Kate to be ill and never for one moment did I think that it was likely to be anything very terrible. She hated it if people made an unnecessary fuss about illness and I decided to leave it for a day or two until after I got back from a charity ball. I had been organizing it and had to be on site in order to deal with any last-minute problems. I saw the awful news of her death in the paper directly I got back and my enquiries met a brick wall both at the club and the hospital. You say you are enquiring into Kate's death? Why is that?'

'Miss Farrant didn't die from natural causes.'

'I don't understand.'

'She was poisoned.'

'Poisoned?'

'Yes. We have spoken to Paul Frampton, Miss Nanson and the secretary, the house-keeper and the security officer at the club and would like to know if you can add anything to what they've told us.'

'I see. How did you discover where I was living?'

'We enquired at the garage in Andover where Kate Farrant bought her new car. They had the phone number of this house and we located it with the satellite navigation system.

We recognized you from the photograph that we obtained from the new offices of The Frampton Trust.'

'And I suppose that the Nanson woman told you that I had been fiddling the petty cash at the charity?'

'Why not start by telling us how you came to be appointed as fundraiser there?'

★ ★ ★

It had seemed to Jane Fisher to be precisely the job she had been looking for. The cause of The Frampton Trust was a particularly worthy one, she liked what she had seen of both Sir Henry and his son Paul when she had paid an informal visit to the offices and the potential for expanding the fundraising and raising the level of public awareness of the charity and putting it all on a more professional basis was very clear. Previously, both had been done mainly by using the old boy network and although that had served well enough when the concern was finding its feet, it was very obvious to her that it needed a major shake-up.

At the interview, she was asked how she would set about putting her ideas into practice and she had plenty of answers, already having had experience with other charities. A properly constituted board was needed, she said, not a large one, but one with an expert in banking, a medical man with experience of dementia, perhaps a retired politician, someone with detailed knowledge of the workings of the NHS, particularly of the social services and a businessman. Of course, she said, Sir Henry would be in the chair with another family member as deputy. Perhaps eight people would be enough. She knew of one charity that received free banking services and perhaps that could be negotiated. As to fundraising itself, there was ample scope for that with the possibility of a ball at which a member of the royal family might agree to come, a sponsored polo match, raffles — and a fun run might also be worth considering.

Jane could see at once that she had the ear of Sir Henry, who obviously liked her enthusiastic approach and nodded at many of the points she made.

It was one thing, though, to outline new ideas at the interview, but quite another to put them into practice once she had started, and she realized at once that it was going to prove a major challenge. The man who had been doing the accounts and auditing on a voluntary basis — he was an old friend of Sir Henry and, before retiring, had run a firm of accountants — was well past it. Paul Frampton, although good at addressing potential donors, was very much under his father's thumb, who very clearly compared him unfavourably with Kate and Adam Farrant, who were the son and daughter of a longstanding friend and were the sort of young people that Sir Henry admired, both being good-looking, successful and dynamic. It was also pretty clear to Jane straight away that Paul's heart wasn't in the project and that he would never have joined had he been capable of standing up to his father, which quite obviously he wasn't. And then there were the day-to-day finances. She gathered that originally Sir Henry had kept a close eye on things, signing all the cheques himself, but then when he became ill, that responsibility passed across to Paul and as he was away quite a bit, it was changed so that she was able to issue cheques up to a maximum of £500 herself.

Her arrival and all the changes had really put Miss Nanson's nose out of joint. The woman had been with Sir Henry right from the beginning and now that she had been largely sidelined, she started to accuse Jane of fiddling the petty cash, of using the charity's stamps for her own use and being extravagant over the events she organized. On one occasion she even hinted that Jane was milking the charity for her own ends. That was the last straw, particularly as she had already taken her courage into her hands and told Sir Henry that the finances were seriously in disarray and that they ought to be dealt with in a more professional manner. Of course she didn't like going behind Paul's back, but he was also very much part of the problem and from Sir Henry's reaction, it was clear that he knew perfectly well that his son wasn't up to it and that he should never have put him in that position. It was then that he told her that he was going to ask Kate Farrant, who was also a chartered accountant, to look into it for him.

As for Miss Nanson, Jane told her exactly what she had said to Sir Henry and what she thought of her insinuations and that if she had anything to do with it, she would be pensioned off. The woman had also hinted that she had been flirting with Paul Frampton and taking advantage of his good nature, but the very idea was so ridiculous that she let that one pass. Finally there was Adam Farrant. The man was clearly greatly admired by Sir Henry; he would occasionally come into the office and whenever he was able, supported the balls, the polo matches and banquets she organized. He was certainly good-looking, always polite and Miss Nanson used to irritate her by hinting that Farrant fancied her and would be a good catch for her. Both ideas were, of course, equally ridiculous. Just before he was due to go to Iraq, the man invited her out to dinner at a restaurant in Sir Henry's hearing, who made it clear to her that he thought it was such a thoughtful and nice gesture and that he would be very disappointed if she refused.

Adam took her to a very fancy place indeed, one very much frequentcd by the in-crowd, and he ordered the very best champagne. He also proved good company and after vaguely remembering him ordering coffee, the rest was a complete blank and she woke up lying on the bed in Paul's flat, bruised, sore and confused, her clothes scattered all over the floor. Paul was away — she knew that Adam was borrowing it while preparing to go to Iraq — and as her head began to clear, she knew exactly what must have happened.

Jane had no family in London and in any case had lost touch with the few relatives she did have, being an only child and both her parents having died young. There was only one person she could think of to whom she might turn and that was Kate Farrant. Sir Henry had admired her even more than her brother; she was both extremely clever and efficient, was a chartered accountant and was making a success of her deceased father's club, of which Sir Henry had been a member for many years. It was he who also asked Kate to make an appraisal of the finances of the charity after the volunteer accountant had finally become totally incapacitated by a stroke.

Luckily, Jane had Kate's mobile phone number in her diary, which providentially she had put in her handbag, as she never liked to be without it, and the woman answered it immediately. She was in her flat at the club and promised to come round immediately. Still feeling out of this world and confused, Jane hardly took in what happened for the rest of that day. She was taken to a private nursing home, checked by a gynaecologist and a physician, given the morning-after pill, sedated and kept in there for several days until all the shock and confusion had settled. It was then that Kate returned and spelt it out in her direct way.

'You were given a drug by that bastard of a brother of mine,' she said, 'and then raped. The good news is that there will be no lasting physical damage at all, you have not been given an infection and you have been given the morning-after pill, so there is no danger of your being pregnant. You need to convalesce properly and you must come to my place in the country to do just that. I will stay with you there for the first few days, then with fresh air and some riding when you're up to it, you'll soon be as right as rain. From what I know of you, you have too robust a personality to allow this to blight your life, but in my judgment, it would be in your interests not to return to Sir Henry's charity.

'It is already quite clear to me that the management of the concern will have to be completely overhauled. Paul's heart isn't in it, the finances need to be put in the hands of competent professionals and more impressive office premises provided.

'I have already had talks with Sir Henry at his request and he is in tune with my ideas. Miss Nanson will have to go and Sir Henry insists on generous terms for her retirement. I told him that she had been spreading rumours about Paul and you, which in my firm belief were unfounded, and he excused that on the grounds that he had promoted her above her ceiling. Moreover, he said that he would never forget how devoted she had been to his wife during her decline and all the time leading up to her death, that she had coped well when the charity was in its infancy and he wished her to have a comfortable retirement. The plan is for Henry to remain as non-executive chairman and he agrees with my suggestion that we should set up a board of suitable people and he has asked me to take the chair. A chief executive will be appointed in place of Miss Nanson and the financial control will be in the hands of an accountant and properly audited.

'Paul is clearly going to resent all this, but his heart has never been in working for the charity and in some ways, despite the loss of face, he may well be relieved. As for yourself, I am convinced that Paul would not tolerate your remaining in post if he is dismissed and, in any case, in view of what that criminal psychopath, my brother, did to you, I suggest that after your convalescence you find a post elsewhere and with my support that shouldn't be difficult. What am I proposing to do about Adam? He has already left for Iraq and the question is whether you would want to face making a formal accusation of rape, having him brought back and then a trial or maybe a court martial at which you would have to give evidence. I have no intention of trying to influence your decision on this, but clearly you either have to do that, or else put it down to experience and put it behind you. Either way, I am more than ready to support you in whatever way I can.'

'And what did you decide to do?'

'Maybe it was wrong of me, but I just couldn't face the inevitable publicity that any accusation on my part would engender, knowing that I would either have the label of a rape victim round my neck or else my account of what happened wouldn't be believed, which would be just as bad. As Kate had promised, she respected my decision and could not have been kinder. She didn't question my account about what had happened, said that the evidence from the hospital was clear, but agreed that the army people were quite likely to close ranks, particularly with his service in Iraq, and it might be in my best interests to look forward rather than back. Whatever happened she would support me and I was welcome to stay here as long as I liked.'

'How did she react to the news that Adam had disappeared, believed killed in Iraq?'

'She didn't mince words, Kate never did. She said that Adam was a monster and that the world would be a better place without him and that her father had thought the same. Evidently there had been some other incident in the past, which had led him to being disowned.'

'What will you do now?'

'There is no point in mincing words. Kate and I fell in love and she told me that she was proposing to leave this cottage to me in her will. I remember very clearly what she said. 'It may seem a bit morbid to be thinking about wills at my age, but accidents and illnesses can come out of the blue — you know what overtook my father — and I want to feel that you are financially secure whatever happens to me.'

'She told me she enjoyed both running the club and her charitable work and it was her aim to keep them going, but our relationship was more important than either of them and that would never be neglected. We were together for a little over a year and I have never been so happy as I was during the time we were together.'

'Do you know the name of Miss Farrant's solicitor?'

'Yes. Kate wanted to keep her personal affairs apart from those of the club and the charity and went to a man who was an old friend of her father — she told me that they were at university together. His card is in a file in her desk and I'll get it for you if you like.'

'Thank you, that would be very helpful.' Sinclair copied down the details and then said: 'What do you plan to do now?'

'I shall stay here for the time being, carry on with my work, and then? Who knows? I have already decided not to attend the funeral and I am quite certain that Kate would have applauded that decision. She told me that she had no friends, only associates, and that none of them really liked her. As for love, apart from her father, she had never really loved anyone until she met me.'

'Do you know what she was proposing to do with the club and the rest of her money if anything did happen to her?'

'No. We didn't discuss that and I would never have asked — it was none of my business.'

Sarah nodded. 'Thank you for being so frank. I take it that your phone number here would be the best way to contact you should the need arise?'

'You'd better have my mobile number as well. I have one or two projects on the go and I decided that keeping busy was the best way for me to cope.'

9

'What did you make of her?' Sinclair asked Sarah as they drove back to London.

'I thought she was very straightforward and telling the truth. We know what Adam Farrant was capable of and that Kate was only too well aware of what he had done before. I can also understand why she advised Jane Fisher not to report it. The publicity would have been enormous and damaging to her; her association with Kate and the charity and Adam's presence in Iraq would have added to it. It wouldn't have done the charity much good either.'

They went to see the solicitor that afternoon. Colin Robertson was a studious-looking man, wearing glasses and with thick greying hair, who looked, Sinclair thought, to be in his early fifties.

'Yes, I knew Richard Farrant very well; we were at Durham together and kept up with each other until his tragic accident. I was away when Kate Farrant was taken ill and died,' he said in his slight Scottish accent, 'and didn't hear about it until I came back to work two days ago. I gather that there has been some concern about the cause of the illness.'

'More than that, I fear,' Sinclair said. 'We have reason to believe that she was poisoned deliberately, although, as I hope you understand, that information is not for public release just yet. We are already looking into the matter and the circumstances surrounding it and it seems possible that her will might have some bearing on the matter.'

'I see.'

Sinclair continued. 'The poison in question is difficult to get hold of. It is no longer used in clinical medicine and its nature and rarity makes an accident virtually out of the question. As to suicide, Miss Farrant had a first-class degree in chemistry and, in our view, the likelihood of self-administration is remote in the extreme; she would have known just how unpleasant the consequences are of taking the chemical. An accident is also highly unlikely and therefore murder is a strong possibility and we are trying to discover a motive, which makes the nature of her will of considerable importance. Added to that, we know that she was extremely wealthy.'

'She was certainly that,' agreed Colin Robertson. 'The will was made almost exactly a year ago and is potentially full of ifs and buts, about which I warned her when it was drawn up. She certainly took the possible difficulties on board, but made it clear that the terms she had set out were in accord with her wishes and that was that.

'One section of it was straightforward enough. She has left a substantial amount of money, her house near Andover, the contents, her two horses and her car to one Jane Fisher, whose address is the same as that of the house. The remainder of her estate, which comprises her property in South Kensington and the remainder of her assets after deduction of inheritance tax, has been left to The Frampton Trust, a registered charity. A condition of the donation is that her club, The Spinning Wheel, at the same address, should be allowed to continue to operate on that site and should be administered by a members committee, on which two officers of the charity, the chairperson and the treasurer, should serve and the charity would benefit from the profits. Miss Farrant was aware that the charity commissioners would also have to be consulted.'

'I see,' said Sarah. 'That sounds like a recipe for controversy. What are the chances of the commissioners agreeing to it?'

'It's not an area with which I am particularly familiar. I did suggest to Miss

Farrant that she or I should sound them out, but she wouldn't have it, saying that she knew all about 'soundings out'. They had a habit of entering the public domain and she was not prepared to accept that risk. 'Should difficulties arise, so be it,' she said. 'I won't be around to worry about them.''

'And what do you think?' asked Sinclair.

A suspicion of a smile appeared fleetingly on the man's face. 'I think this is going to involve a good deal of time and work, except for the provision for Miss Fisher, which should be straightforward enough.'

'No doubt the inheritance tax will be considerable,' said Sarah.

'The charity being a beneficiary will mitigate it to some extent, but the issues involved will undoubtedly be complex and I wouldn't be surprised if it took a good deal of time to settle the whole matter.'

'Rather more than somewhat would be my guess,' Sinclair said, raising his eyebrows.

'You may well be right.'

'What about the staff of the club and the members while all this is going on?' Sarah asked.

'Miss Farrant thought about that, too,' Robertson told her. 'She instructed this firm to take over administration of the club while the provisions of her will were being discussed, allowing the staff to be paid and the members to continue their activities according to the rules prevailing at the time. I understand that it has been closed for the time being.'

'Yes,' Sinclair said. 'We haven't finished our enquiries yet and it won't be able to open again until we have done so. What is likely to happen if the trustees of the charity refuse to take it on?'

'The entire estate will go to Miss Fisher and it would then be up to her to decide what to do with it.'

'The whole thing sounds to me like a minefield.' Sinclair smiled at the man on the other side of the desk. 'Rather you than me. We are meeting with some of the staff tomorrow and we will have to tell them something about the future. Any suggestions?'

'Who is dealing with the situation locally at present?' asked the solicitor.

'A Miss Corsie, who is the secretary there.'

'I will write her a formal letter telling her that the administration of the club will be in the hands of this firm for the time being and that I will be arranging a meeting with her in the near future.'

'Right,' said Sarah. 'My colleague and I will be going to the club again tomorrow and I

238

take it that it would be in order for us to tell Miss Corsie that you will be contacting her before too long? We will not, of course, reveal the contents of the will.'

The man nodded. 'I have no problem with that and I look forward to hearing from you about any progress in your enquiries shortly.'

★　★　★

'I've had another idea,' Sarah said the next morning, when they were sitting at breakfast.

'Good Lord, not another. What brain food have you been taking on the quiet?' Sinclair grinned at her as he skilfully evaded the anticipated kick under the table.

'I realize that it's a bit of a long shot but I'm sure it's worth following up and when I explained my ideas to Tredgold yesterday, he agreed to my approaching a woman with the exotic name of Cressida Lake, who is an expert in the field I had in mind, with a view to her accompanying us on a visit to the club. I thought we should do it as soon as possible and she's available this morning. He doesn't have a great deal of time for her main line of work or what I was suggesting, but you know what he's like.'

'I do, only too well.'

'Anyway, she is happy to come there with

us and do her best.'

'What exactly have you in mind?'

Sinclair listened without interrupting as she explained in detail.

'We've got three more days before Tyrrell is finished with those meetings he was telling us about and if I'm right, we have at least a chance of sorting all this out within that time. What do you think?'

'It's not something I'd noticed, let alone even considered, but I don't see what we've got to lose. If you're right, it also opens up other possible lines of enquiry.'

'That's what I thought, too.'

★ ★ ★

It was a few minutes after nine that morning that Sarah telephoned The Spinning Wheel Club and spoke to Jill Corsie.

'We thought it was time to bring you up to date with our enquiries. May we call in at about ten o'clock?'

'Yes, of course,' said Jill.

'There will be three of us on this occasion. We may need to go back into the flat as well, but shouldn't take up too much of your time.'

When they were arrived, they were shown into Jill Corsie's office by Bert Powell, the security officer.

'The most important new development we have to report,' Sarah said, after she had introduced Cressida Lake, 'is that we have managed to locate Miss Farrant's will, which was lodged with a different solicitor from the one that did the conveyancing when she took over this club following her father's death. She drew it up when she took over the chair of The Frampton Trust.

'It is important for you to understand that the will has yet to be proved and probate granted nor have the charity had an opportunity to state whether they are prepared to accept the conditions of the will or not. Any immediate questions?'

'What about our current staff and their salaries?'

'Miss Farrant specified that everyone should be retained and paid at their current rates until the future management has been agreed.'

'Does that include the croupiers?'

'I imagine so, but the solicitor hopes to meet you as soon as he has checked the full implications of the will both on the short and long term and I would suggest that you prepare a list of questions that you wish to be answered. You should also understand that the charity commissioners will have to be involved and it may well take some time to settle all the issues involved.'

'Yes, I understand that, but the news for us is better than I expected.'

'I should also point out that there is one other problem. You see, there will have to be an inquest and, as yet, the pathologist has not been able to establish with any certainty the cause of Miss Farrant's severe gastroenteritis which resulted in her death. It is clearly in everyone's interest for that to be settled as soon as possible, but I am not able to say when that will be.'

'Well, thank you for taking the trouble to come round to explain the situation.'

Sarah gave the woman a smile. 'The solicitor should be contacting you very soon and I'm sure he will make the legal aspects much clearer than I am able to do.'

'Excellent. At least it gives us hope of a future for the club. How about a cup of coffee?'

Sarah looked round at both Sinclair and Cressida Lake and when both of them smiled and nodded, she accepted, saying, 'That would be most welcome.'

To Sarah's surprise, in view of the fact that Cressida Lake's replies to their previous questions had been mostly monosyllabic, she proved to be a good conversationalist, including not only Jill Corsie but also the housekeeper and security officer. She was interested in the house, asking about the date that it had been built, if there had been any interesting former occupants, the name of the architect, how many original features still existed and how large the original garden had been. It was Mrs Grant who was able to supply a lot of the answers. Richard Farrant had been doing some research on the building just before he was killed and she had helped him with collating the information, old photographs and drawings he had collected.

'Do you know what has happened to all that information?' Sinclair asked.

'I expect it's somewhere in the flat in the basement,' the woman said. 'I did ask Kate once if she was going to put it together and perhaps make a book of it all and she said that she was just too busy with the charity and the club, but that perhaps she might find time later on. I'm not sure, though, that she didn't just say that to keep me quiet. You see, like a lot of young people these days, I don't think she was much interested in the past.'

They left half an hour later and as Sinclair negotiated the traffic, Sarah turned towards Cressida Lake, who was sitting in the back.

'Any views?' she asked.

'I'll write a report for you as soon as I get back.'

Back in their office at the Yard, after they had dropped the woman off, their secretary told them that while they were away, a Mrs Cassidy had rung to say that she had found something that might be of help in finding her daughter and after returning her call, they decided to go to see her again that afternoon.

★ ★ ★

'I had a note from my bank a few days after you had come to see me telling me that they were reviewing the arrangements for items of mine in their safe deposit boxes,' the woman said when they were sitting in the living room. 'They told me that they were planning to increase the charges and asked me if I would care to review the contents as it was such a long time since I had been there. I did so and I found this cardboard box, which I had forgotten about, and when I opened it I remembered what you had said and wondered if it would be any help in finding out what has happened to Pauline. This dressing-table set, which, as you see, consists of a mirror, brush and comb, has been in the family for a very long time and I inherited them from my mother and passed them on to

Pauline. She did use them for a time in her early teens, but then she upset me by saying that they were 'naff' and 'not cool' and that her friends would laugh at her if they knew that she was using them. The first time I saw them was when my grandmother showed them to me and told me that they were very precious and if they were ever to come to me to be sure to look after them carefully. I've always thought they were valuable, but one hears so much these days about fakes that I wondered about that. I suppose I ought to have had them valued by an expert, but I had no intention of selling them and I never got round to it.'

Sarah nodded. 'Might I take a look?'

'Of course.'

Sarah put on her plastic gloves and took the top off the box. Inside was a silver hairbrush, mirror and tortoiseshell comb.

'What do you think, Mark? You know about these things.'

'Not all that much, but a little.'

Also wearing gloves and using his pocket magnifying glass, Sinclair lifted up the mirror and examined the handle carefully.

'Well, as I said, I'm no expert and I would suggest you get a reputable valuer to look at them. They are certainly sterling silver and you would be able to get the year from the date mark, which is clearly visible. I think they are probably late Georgian and so at least two hundred years old. May I look at the brush?'

'Of course.'

'Is your daughter Pauline's hair fair?'

'Yes, like mine was until it went grey. Hers was almost white when she was a small child and, although it did get a bit darker later on, it remained blonde. Any of her hairs still left in the brush are likely to have come from when she last used it when she was in her early teens. I added them to the other bits of silver I owned, some napkin rings and a cigarette box that belonged to my late husband.'

'How thoroughly did you clean the bristles before putting the brush away?' Sarah asked.

'I can't remember. I certainly wouldn't have washed it and it's so old that I'm sure I would have been careful not to do anything too vigorous.'

Sarah put on her plastic gloves from her shoulder bag and lifted it up, looking at it closely with Sinclair's lens. Very carefully, she removed several of the fair hairs from the bristles and put them in the plastic bottle. She smiled at the woman.

'That's all that we need. It's a long shot, but tests on those hairs may just possibly be of help in giving us a clue to your daughter's whereabouts now. I promise we'll get in touch with you if we have any luck in finding her.'

★ ★ ★

'Now that we've come this far, why don't we go on to Basingstoke and have a word with the man who gave Jill Corsie a reference when she applied for the job at Farrant's club? Provided, of course, that he's still there,' Sarah said. 'I made a note of his number as there are one or two things I wanted to check.'

'Good idea. Why not give the firm a ring on your mobile?'

They were in luck. Michael Baron, the man who had given the reference, was now the managing director of the firm Maxton's Instruments Limited, which had offices on the outskirts of the town in the same building as that in which the manufacturing processes were carried out. They met him that afternoon.

'Yes, of course I remember Jill Corsie very well indeed. May I ask why you are interested in her?'

'One Kate Farrant, the owner of a club in London at which Miss Corsie works, died under unusual circumstances there recently and we are making a check on all the people employed there as a start. There is bound to be media interest as she was in the chair of a large charity and was also the daughter of Richard Farrant. You may have heard of him. He was killed in a powerboat accident in the States.'

'Yes, I remember seeing the pictures on TV and what jogged my memory was finding a letter from him asking for a reference for Jill Corsie when she applied for a job at his club. Well, all I can say is that I had nothing but respect for her. She was not only a highly efficient secretary, but a good deal more than that. After your phone call I got her file out and I have it here. I see that it was in 1998 that the advertisement went out and we had a number of applications for it.

'Jill was quite different from the usual run of applicants. Not only was she much older than the others, but she also had an interesting background.' He opened the file in front of him. 'She was educated at a comprehensive school and was obviously very bright, getting a place at Bristol University, where she obtained an upper second-class honours degree in chemistry, which in itself was attractive to me. You see, in those days, I needed to send out a good few letters with technical content, which your average secretary finds extremely difficult to take on

248

board, and in the past I had had to send them on a course in order to familiarize them with the jargon. That didn't apply in Jill's case. I was also looking for someone to take minutes at meetings here at which I was in the chair and her knowledge of scientific language was an added bonus.'

'You must have had a secretary before her. Did she retire?' asked Sarah.

'Yes, on health grounds. She was only in her early fifties, but developed a chronic gastric upset, which no one seemed to be able to diagnose and she had to give up work. To be brutally honest, I wasn't too sorry to see her go. She was a perfectly competent typist, but she lacked the degree of initiative that I needed and she found the technical aspects of the work, such as taking messages, difficult, as she lacked any sort of comprehension of chemistry. I had in fact inherited her from my predecessor, who was essentially an administrator, and when he retired the company was after someone with technical know-how and that turned out to be me.

'I decided to give her a one-year contract in the first instance, largely because she had almost no experience of work as a secretary, although she did have a glowing reference from the woman who ran the course in shorthand and typing which she attended. Of course, even then, shorthand skills were beginning to disappear, but they do have advantages and I was used to having a secretary proficient in them.'

'What had she done in the way of work before coming here?'

'Her history was a sad one in many ways. You see, she had not long finished her university degree course and had just started her first job with a drugs firm, when her father was killed in a road accident — a drunken driver mounted the pavement and knocked him down. He suffered severe injuries and died at the scene. Sad though that was, in itself it need not have interfered with her career, had her mother not already been seriously incapacitated by multiple sclerosis. Jill's father had done all the caring — by the time he died, his wife needed to be fed and bathed — and the choices were hospital, which proved almost impossible to achieve, other than in the very short term, a nursing home, which would have been prohibitively expensive, or Jill leaving her job and looking after her mother at home. She had little choice, really, and stuck it out for ten years or so until her mother died.

'There she was, in her middle thirties, the little money her father had left mostly swallowed up despite the state allowances, and she had become socially isolated. Did she go into a gloom? No, she didn't; she wasn't going to settle for some dead-end job and with what money was left took a secretarial course with computer studies and applied to us, hoping that her background in chemistry might overcome her lack of experience. I was impressed by her get-up-and-go attitude on top of her knowledge of chemistry and that's why I decided to give her an extended trial.

'I never regretted the decision to appoint her. She was efficient, excellent on the keyboard, reliable, punctual and never ill. She understood the technical language and the chemistry of our work. I took her with me to conferences and her notes on the papers presented were invaluable as it meant that she provided cover for some of the satellite presentations, which were of interest to us, while I attended the main ones.'

'I gather that your firm makes medical imaging equipment.'

'Yes, that's right.'

'Why did Miss Corsie leave her job here?'

'She wanted to go to London — she was not getting much of a social life in Basingstoke — and the job she applied for was not only better paid than the one here, but included a flat on site, which was in an attractive location in South Kensington.'

'Did she keep in contact with you?'

'We exchanged Christmas cards for a year or two, that's all.'

'Well,' said Sinclair, 'many thanks for your help. Any chance of having a look round your factory?'

'Any particular reason?'

Sinclair smiled. 'No, just that we're always on the lookout for things outside our experience and if the opportunity arises, it's an interesting way of widening our knowledge and painless, too, at least for us.'

'No problem. Jake Field is the chap for you — he suffers from an excess of wanting to please.'

Baron was right. The young man wanted to show them everything — how the manufacturing process worked, what the products were used for — and he also introduced them to the people operating the various machines.

'I asked for that, didn't I?' Sinclair said when they were back in the car.

'Yes, but we got what we wanted, didn't we?'

10

It was early on the following Monday morning that the two detectives met Roger Tyrrell in his office.

'Sorry to have abandoned you,' he said, 'but at least I now have the time to put my mind to the Kate Farrant case. Any progress?'

'We're pretty well there, sir, largely thanks to Sarah. I'd like her to bring you up to date, sir, if that's all right,' said Sinclair.

'Sounds intriguing. Carry on.'

Sarah nodded. 'As you already know, sir, investigation into Kate's death only started because Tredgold did the post mortem and discovered that she had been poisoned by thallium, something that had not been picked up at the hospital. Death in that way is particularly unpleasant and as Kate was very well versed in chemistry, having obtained a first-class degree in the subject, self-administration seemed highly unlikely. She also appeared to have had a very robust personality with no suggestion of having had depressive episodes in the past.

'It also seemed probable she was given the poison while in The Spinning Wheel Club, which she owned. Its effects come on within hours of ingestion and we found out that she had not left the club for at least twelve hours, if not longer, before she was taken ill. I won't go into the details, but we discovered that the thallium must have been put in one of the cartons of grapefruit juice that she liked to drink, which were stored in the pantry of the club. It seems probable that Kate being poisoned on that day or more likely that evening was a matter of chance, depending on which day that particular carton had been taken down from the store to her flat. If we were right it also followed that the poisoner must have been someone with regular access to the club, suggesting that either one of the staff or a member of the club was responsible.

'Apart from Kate, only Mrs Grant, the housekeeper, had access to the flat and she also kept the refrigerator stocked. We believe that, quite unwittingly, she was the one to take the poisoned juice down there. Having been at the club for at least twenty years, she was obviously trusted, being the only person apart from Kate to know the combination of the key pad on the door from the lobby of the club to her flat, using it to clean daily when Kate was in residence. She seemed neither to have had any possible motive for killing Kate, nor the background and expertise to have had access to a rare element such as thallium.

'A number of people had good reason to dislike or even hate Kate Farrant and I suggest that we consider them in turn. There was Adam, her twin brother, who was clearly a psychopath, who had been expelled from the same school that Kate had attended for abusing two of the pupils both physically and the girl sexually. This proved to be a very complicated affair as Kate was responsible for it coming to the attention of the authorities and she also appears to have been having an affair with the girl's housemistress, one Pauline Cassidy, who had been spying on some of the girls in her house, setting up a surveillance camera in one of the bathrooms, and was summarily dismissed as a result.

'Revenge must surely have been on Adam's mind. He was further implicated in the drugging and rape of one of the fundraisers at the charity, of which Kate became chairperson, and finally disappeared in Iraq while in the SAS following his involvement in the beating of a young Iraq girl. Did he get back to England to get his revenge on Kate? We thought it possible, but unlikely, and poisoning would not have been his style.

'There was Paul Frampton, son of the founder of the charity for which he worked.

His heart clearly wasn't in it, but even so did he resent Kate so much when she took over the reins that he decided to poison her? It is true that he was a member of her club, had been working in Hungary where thallium might have been available and it was in his flat that Adam had raped the woman, who was working as a fundraiser at the charity, but we didn't think he was a murderer.

'Margaret Nanson, Sir Henry Frampton's former secretary, clearly liked to give the impression that she was the one to have looked after Sir Henry's wife devotedly and then propped up the old man afterwards and suggested to him the idea of setting up the charity. Paul poo-pooed that idea, but did concede that the woman had done an excellent job in looking after his mother. She may have resented Kate Farrant sweeping in and taking over, but we couldn't see her poisoning her, nor would she have had the opportunity to do so.

'Then there was the fundraiser, Jane Fisher, who was raped by Adam and also lost her job. However, it seems that Kate went out of her way to help her and it appears that the two women fell in love and had set up an establishment together away from the club. It is also true that Kate left her substantial assets in her will, but we were impressed by her as being both truthful and devastated by her lover's death.

'Finally, we come to Jill Corsie. She was obviously very competent at her job and there is little doubt that Kate had great confidence in her. You may remember, sir, that when I was working on that prostitution racket involving girls from Eastern Europe, I went on a course on facial recognition and the ability of disreputable plastic surgeons to alter appearance, which was being practised on some of the women running the racket and the girls themselves. Had it not been for that, I doubt if I would have noticed that Jill Corsie had had work done on her; the skin on her forehead was unnaturally tight for someone of her age and her nose looked rather too narrow for the shape of the rest of her face. Anyway, largely out of curiosity, I got Jack Pocock to go into her flat and he obtained some hairs from a brush in there. There was no match on the database, but the breakthrough came when Mrs Cassidy, the mother of the disgraced housemistress, whom we had previously interviewed and who had not seen her daughter since she had left the school, rang us to say that, at her bank, she had found an old silver hairbrush belonging to her daughter. We had some hairs on it tested and that was it. The DNA on them was identical to those that Jack had had tested.

'We chased up a reference that she had given when applying for the job at the club when Kate's father was in charge and that's how we found that previously she had been working in a factory at which thallium was used in the manufacture of optical instruments. Finally, Tredgold put me on to a woman, one Cressida Lake, who is an expert on facial recognition, and I made up some story and took her to the club to meet Jill Corsie. She confirmed my suspicion that the woman had had extensive plastic surgery to her nose and ears, botox to her forehead and that she was wearing tinted contact lenses and had dyed her hair.'

'So there's no doubt that this woman and Pauline Cassidy are one and the same?' asked Tyrell.

'Yes and she clearly had a motive for getting her own back on the girl, Kate Farrant, whom she considered had betrayed her all those years ago. As a result of all that, I believe we now have enough to charge her with Kate Farrant's murder,' said Sarah.

'What's your view, Mark?'

'I have no doubt myself that what Sarah has discovered makes it absolutely certain that Pauline Cassidy and Jill Corsie are one and the same person and I also believe that she murdered Kate Farrant. However, we can't prove that she stole thallium from that firm in Basingstoke and I haven't enough experience of murder trials to know what chances a really good barrister might have of mounting a successful defence. However, I don't see how we are going to be able to obtain any more evidence and I go along with Sarah's view that she should be charged now, not least because she has already done one disappearing act and may well have another contingency plan up her sleeve. We also have to accept that she might even now suspect that we are getting close to her and my belief is that we may be near to running out of time before she disappears again.'

'You both put the situation very clearly and congratulations on some excellent work. The only contribution I have to make is that I am quite satisfied that Rupert Chester's alibi holds up and I think we can eliminate him. I need to consider the case very carefully myself and consult our legal people for their view of the likely success of a prosecution for murder. I agree that a decision must be taken as soon as possible. I'll come back to you very shortly.'

★ ★ ★

Jill Corsie was convinced that she had got away with it when she heard that Kate Farrant had died and there had been nothing in the papers to suggest that there was any suspicion that it had been due to anything other than natural causes. She liked working at the club, she got on well with the rest of the staff and all along a bonus had been the succession of pretty and desirable girls who were appointed as croupiers. It also seemed very likely that the future of the club being owned by the Frampton charity was assured and she saw herself as playing a more important role in its management in the future.

She knew, though, that should poisoning in Kate Farrant's case be suspected, then a search of the building might well be instituted. She was not worried about Kate's flat, being certain that no one would suspect or even criticize her motives in arranging for a thorough clean-up down there and the disposal of the soiled bedclothes, mattress and carpet. There were, though, one or two things to be done elsewhere. Remembering only too vividly what had happened at Brantley College, she removed the camera she had attached to the light assembly in the croupiers' shower room and took it and the tapes to a safe deposit box.

The arrival of the two detectives had been a worry initially, but not for very long. Both of them were pleasant and polite, didn't appear unduly concerned about the cause of Kate Farrant's death and a bonus had been the young female police inspector. She was just the type that Jill Corsie liked most of all: pretty, well covered and cuddly — there was no other word for it. She also had a nice line in blushes, which, when Jill saw it disappear below the neckline of her dress, fired her imagination as to where else it might have spread.

She had had a friendly meeting with Kate Farrant's solicitor the previous day and had no reason to suspect anything untoward until she heard the screech of the metal gates leading to the street in front of the garage and, looking out of the window, saw the police van backing into the short drive. She had an instinct that it was all over and if that was the case, she had no intention of rotting in jail, or even worse in a secure mental hospital — but the moment had not quite come to give up altogether. What direct evidence might the police have up their sleeve? None as far as she could see, but that didn't mean that she should neglect to make contingency plans. She went to her dressing table, took the container out of her sponge bag and eased the very small capsule

261

into her left nostril, anchoring it with a twist of cotton wool. She examined her face in the mirror, tilted her head back slightly and after pushing the cotton wool a fraction further upwards, smiled at herself and set off down the stairs.

Her arrest and the caution, delivered by the young woman, came almost straight away and as she could see no way of taking advantage of that situation, she said absolutely nothing either there, or in the van on the way to the police station, and did not react to the offer of a phone call to her solicitor. The strip search, though, was another matter. Sarah Prescott was present, and that gave her the opportunity she had hoped for. It was too much to hope that the young woman would carry out the search herself, but it was perfectly clear that she was finding the whole thing both embarrassing and distasteful. Apart from wanting to milk the situation as much as possible, Jill was also determined to distract them as much as she could, in order to reduce the risk of their finding the capsule in her nostril.

As the female officer ran her hands over her breasts and lifted them up slightly, she opened her eyes wide, rolled them around and gave a theatrical shudder. She could see that she was getting to both the women. The searcher did continue, despite her more and more suggestive movements, but the detective, although she didn't look away, was clearly profoundly embarrassed by the whole business, particularly when, near the end of the search, Jill let out a theatrical groan and moved her head from side to side, at the same time closing her eyes. A further reward was the blush that spread up the young woman's neck, but to Jill's disappointment, she didn't look away.

She knew that she had won when she was led to her cell, now wearing a gown taped at the back, the capsule still lying undetected up her nose. She was convinced that the best chance of being able to retrieve it without being seen would be when the prison officer left the cell for the first time. She was sitting on the side of the bed and in the few moments when the woman was out of sight, going through the door and relocking it, in one swift movement she retrieved the capsule and held it in her hand.

Putting both the capsule and the cotton wool into her mouth, Pauline Cassidy lay on her side, reliving the extraordinary sense of triumph she had experienced when Kate Farrant, deathly pale, had been carried out of the club by the ambulance men. She smiled and then swallowed.

★ ★ ★

'Potassium cyanide!' Tredgold said, giving the three detectives on the other side of his desk one of his most vulpine smiles. 'So, she got the better of you in the end, did she? I gather you've been in the vanguard in this case, my dear. What's your reaction to it all?'

'Considerable relief,' Sarah said. 'I'm sorry for the prison staff — successful suicide of a prisoner is always upsetting for those involved — but I'm quite sure that that woman would have been able to manipulate both staff and inmates and, in my view, would have ruled the roost very quickly had she been given the opportunity. She was clearly a clever, resourceful and utterly ruthless woman, changing her appearance, insinuating herself into The Spinning Wheel Club and biding her time before poisoning Kate Farrant. I don't know how long she might have remained in prison, but based on other cases, I suspect that she would probably have been released eventually.'

'Any comments, Sinclair?'

'I agree and I venture to suggest that not every forensic pathologist would have picked up that Kate Farrant had died from the effects of thallium and that may well have been why that woman selected it as a poison. After all, it is not in general use now, either as a pesticide or in medical treatment — I gather that at one time it had a place in the management of ringworm of the scalp.'

'Is there no limit to the man's erudition? Anyway, thank you for the compliment, kind sir, and at the risk of boasting, you may well be right.' The man smiled and for once, Sinclair thought, it came close to seeming genuine. 'And while we're handing out praise, between the two of you, I believe that the sleuthing deserves a commendation or two.'

'It was mainly due to picking up the fact that Jill Corsie had had cosmetic surgery and getting the critical DNA sample,' Sarah said.

'Interesting that. You have sharp eyes, my dear, and Miss Lake was full of admiration for your observational skill and perspicacity. Fine word that and I don't often have the opportunity to air it. You've been very quiet, Tyrrell. Anything bothering you?'

'On the contrary. All I have to say is well done to all of you.'

'Does that include the demise of the guilty party?'

'I consider that that point has already had more than enough of an airing whatever those sections of the press, who are ever ready to cast stones at us and the prison service, may have written.' Tredgold let out a loud guffaw. 'As ever, my dear fellow, you demonstrate your uncanny mastery of the last word.'